“Like water which can clearly mirror the sky and the trees only as long as its surface is undisturbed, the mind can only reflect the true image of the self when it is tranquil and wholly relaxed.”
Indra Devi

Did you know...

In the UK, 1 in 4 people will experience some sort of mental illness at some point in their lives, that's 25%, ¼ or 15 million of us!

The World Health Organization estimate 2% of the world population are or have experienced depression.

Chocolate contains a brain chemical called phenylethlamine, a mild mood elevator (you have to eat about 25 bars to get the full effects though!) – perhaps that's why some people feel addicted to it.

According to the World Health Organization, a third of the world population are smokers – addicted to tobacco.

In 2005, the health development agency, suggested that over 8 million people across England and Wales experience an alcohol use disorder – that's 29% of the population!

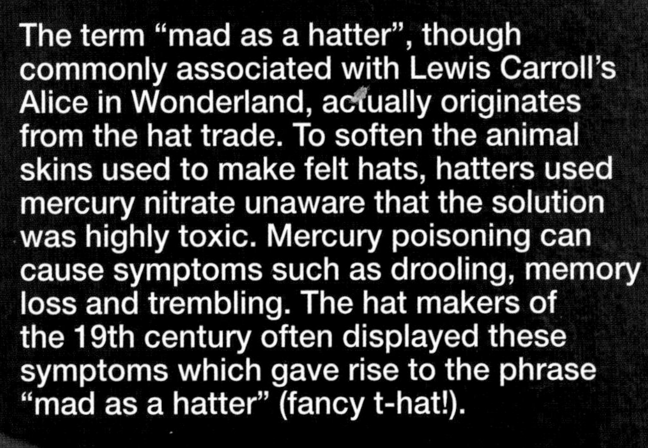

The term “mad as a hatter”, though commonly associated with Lewis Carroll’s Alice in Wonderland, actually originates from the hat trade. To soften the animal skins used to make felt hats, hatters used mercury nitrate unaware that the solution was highly toxic. Mercury poisoning can cause symptoms such as drooling, memory loss and trembling. The hat makers of the 19th century often displayed these symptoms which gave rise to the phrase “mad as a hatter” (fancy t-hat!).

The word “lunatic” dates back to the 12th century where episodes of “insanity” were believed to be triggered by the phases of the moon.

The world's oldest "lunatic asylum" is in London. The Bethlehem Royal Hospital started admitting patients for treatment in 1403: they were called "Bedlamites" – hence the word bedlam!

The term "batty", used to describe someone with a mental illness, comes from the surname of William Battie, a 17th century physician.

The word "hysteria" comes from the Greek word "hystera", meaning uterus (ever heard of a bloke described as hysterical?).

The straitjacket was invented in 1720 – by the French!

Foreword by Darren Bottrill

MBACP (Accred)
Future Days Counselling
Psychotherapy & Supervision
01726 77569
Project Director, Nightlink
Cornwall's Emotional support
Helpline 0808 8000306

The subject of "Emotional Health" has become especially popular over the last 10 years. The Health and Wellbeing sections of bookshops and internet book sites are full of publications on how to change your life, by scores of different authors, all trying to tap into a booming market by promising you eternal happiness, success and even wealth! No such promises here…

What we have here is essentially an Emotional Health dictionary containing an A-Z of mental health terms, some you may have heard of and hopefully many you have not.

This book is an extensive introduction to the world of your mind and its intrinsic connection to your body.

There's no one single concept, no key to success and no tips on alchemy!

If you're interested in beginning to learn more about your holistic self then this is a great place to start.

This book is written in clear, easy to understand English with a colourful and humorous presentation.

Many of us dream of writing a book, so when Emma approached me with the idea, I could be forgiven for dismissing it as another pipe dream.

However, Emma is not just another dreamer.

She has the incredible drive required to see a project through to its completion.

Writing a book requires immense dedication and determination. Having proved herself by writing The Little Book of Cornwall there was no question of "if" only of "when."

Additionally, Emma has the advantage of having walked the walk. She has poignantly experienced emotional distress and in this book she talks from the heart, as well as utilising extensive research and drawing on the knowledge of mental health professionals.

I have worked in Mental Health for 10 years, both as Clinical Psychotherapist and as a provider of non-statutory mental health services.

I have worked with every conceivable type of person with issues ranging from mild anxiety or depression through to severe psychosis and suicidal idealisation.

What links us all is physis - and I invite you to look that up herein!

Physis is the natural drive to health that resides within all creatures. The variance is the time taken on each individual journey.

So while there are no promises here of eternal happiness and definitely no "quick fix" offerings, it is with much hope that this book will bring you some new awarenesses that may well speed your physis along.

Enjoy!

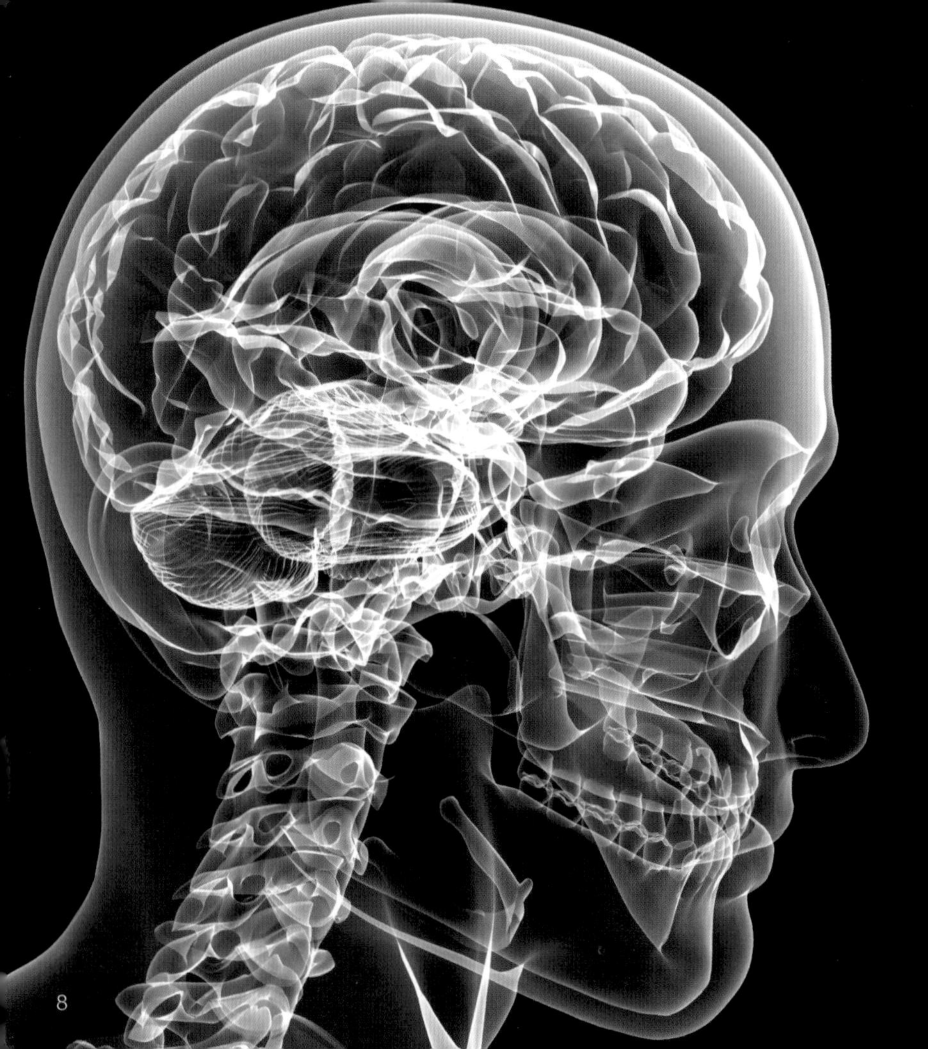

“Limitations live only in our minds. But if we use our imagination, our possibilities become limitless.”
Jamie Paolinetti

The mind…

The mind, the beautiful mind, chief exec. of the human body; in part understood but for most of us, the mind is still one of life's greatest mysteries.

Our mind is the most powerful part of our body; it generates our thoughts and our sense of reality; it gives us our meaning and makes sense of the world.

Our mind sets us up for how we get on, how we communicate and how we behave, how we feel and how we think.

Our mind is the source of our pleasure and our pain. Our individual mysteries are held deep within it, lived out through our patterns, values and beliefs.

Our mind is part of our brain – our central computer – which creates the chemicals that manage our mood, and which holds our memory and helps us recall it. It enables us to move, to pay attention, to fight/flee/freeze or rest.

Above all, the mind is who we are; it processes and enables our responses to life. Our mind gives us our connection to our body, our soul, to others and to the world around us. So, the more we understand our mind and why we do the things we do, the more power we have to change many aspects of our life.

Our minds, like are bodies, are unique and different. Some of our minds are strong and resilient, others can be sensitive and more vulnerable in life.

When our mind is well we feel healthy and positive, at ease with others and at ease with ourselves. If our mind is pressured we can feel distress or at worst we experience dis-ease. Addiction, anxiety, depression and stress are all symptoms of a mind that's unhappy or holding on to old hurts or unresolved issues.

At times, the state of our mind may be such that we disconnect, withdraw from our life, feeling overwhelmed or indeed out of our mind.

If we do feel this way, the sooner we seek help and get the right treatment, the sooner we can begin to understand our situation, find support and overcome or begin to manage our condition.

Psychological and emotional dis-ease present symptoms that can't be seen and when we can't see something it's much harder to understand it.

Psychological terms such as "depression" , "schizophrenia" or "personality disorder" carry many stigmas, these stigmas can create fear as well as mis-understanding.

Terms for mental or emotional dis-ease carry many stereotypes or societal assumptions. Words like "looney", "nutter" and "wierdo" are often used to describe someone experiencing emotional or psychological distress which increases our fear furthermore.

We forget that behind every term, description or condition there is an individual, a person and a human being just like you or I.

Society and to some extent, the media, don't always see or portray the individual, rather the condition or label they carry. This also arouses fear and it certainly doesn't increase our understanding of someone or what they might be experiencing.

Well, The Little Book of the Mind has been written to increase understanding. In A-Z order, this book explores all the different reasons why all of our minds can struggle from time to time.

It unpacks and outlines all the different types of psychological and emotional discomforts, theories as to how they develop and indeed how they can be overcome.

You'll also find the different types of treatments, therapies and qualities we can adopt if we want to manage or overcome our illness, get to know ourselves better or grow in peace of mind.

We're all different, what works as a treatment or theory for one might not work for another.

Some of our minds need long-term medication, some might find talking the route to relief, some of us might want to develop our self-awareness or some of us may want to understand our thinking.

Whatever we want, our mind can help us but only if we want it and are prepared to explore and understand what might be at the root of our discomfort or preventing our growth. Our experiences can expand and develop our mind, but only if we are open to learning. We cannot find ourselves if we don't admit we're lost.

I've lost my mind a number of times (I don't know where it went but I knew I'd get it back!). I've experienced a couple of "nervous breakdowns", "anxiety" ,"clinical depression" and "psychosis". As part of my recovery journey I explored many different treatments from antidepressants to the "talking cure". I've read a great deal and participated in a number of courses in counselling and psychotherapy.

All of my experiences and learning have led to this book along with the words, theories and expertise of others.

We live in changing times, now more than ever we need to be confident, flexible, adaptable and resilient. The economic, social and natural environment are constantly changing, who knows what challenges may lie ahead.

A mind that is calm, clear and strong can support us through challenges; it's the tool that enables our creativity, helps us change and deliver our dreams.

If our mind is fragile life can feel like storm, we feel blown about, lost, confused or out of control. If this is the case, the more we understand how our mind works, how we think and why we feel and do what we do, the better placed we are to use our heads to change our story and in time create what we want for our life.

The chance to change and find peace of mind begins with understanding and acceptance...

Acceptance

"That which we resist will persist." Anon

Acceptance is important to all of us – we all need to feel accepted and acceptable. But most of all, we need to accept ourselves. Choosing to accept who we are and our situation helps ease our mind and opens the door to change.

"Acceptance is not submission, it is acknowledgement of the facts of a situation, then deciding what you're going to do about it." Kathleen Casey Thiesen

Some things in life are hard to accept; the loss of a loved one, job or relationship, or coming to terms with addiction or an eating disorder. But as we accept our situation, we can begin to understand it and ourselves, and move forward.

"Understanding is the first step to acceptance, and only with acceptance can there be recovery." JK Rowling.

If we can't accept we've got a problem with alcohol, it's unlikely we'll recover from it. (We can't make a comeback if we haven't been anywhere!) If our past's been painful or stained with regret, by accepting what's gone we can start new beginnings.

As we begin to accept and embrace who we are (and where we've come from), we can develop peace of mind. Life needn't be a drama.

"As you become more clear about who you really are, you'll be better able to decide what's best for you." Oprah Winfrey

A
“Only by acceptance of the past can you alter it.” TS Eliot

A

Acting out

"Acting out" gives the mind relief. If we've unresolved issues or grief held within, we act out in relation to these things in an attempt to release their emotional energy.

When we "act out" we use inauthentic behaviour to work through unresolved issues or release emotional hurts.

We may become angry when really we're scared, or we may pretend we're happy when really we're sad. Our Western society encourages us to admit to some emotions rather than others, which ones often depending on whether we're male or female.

We're not always aware of when and why we "act out". Our behaviour is driven by the unconscious part of our mind, the part that's beyond our awareness and outside our control.

As we begin to explore the back of our mind, we can let go of old feelings and patterns of behaviour and adopt new and healthier ways to express how we feel.

It might take time or the help of a therapist, but by exploring and acknowledging our unresolved issues, we can begin to understand ourselves, heal and develop behaviour that's more in keeping with our true feelings. (Then life needn't be a such performance!).

"Healing takes courage, and we all have courage, even if we have to dig a little to find it."
Tori Amos

Addiction

You know you're "addicted" to caffeine if:

a) **You grind your coffee beans in your mouth.**
b) **You sleep with your eyes open.**
c) **You can take a picture of yourself from 10 feet away without the timer.**
d) **You haven't blinked since the last lunar eclipse!**

Action on Addiction claim that 1 in 3 people in the UK suffer from addiction.

From the first taste of alcohol to our first "one night stand", from choosing to gamble or smoking tobacco - we may not choose to become addicted but the choices we make can lead to dependency.

The 'high', excitement or pleasure we get from taking drugs, smoking, drinking, gambling or having sex makes us feel good – but when that feeling subsides we may feel deflated, down or anxious. When we're addicted, it's not the 'high' we're after – it's relief the drug or activity gives us from the anxiety of withdrawal.

Some people are described as having "addictive personalities" – more prone to seek outside stimulation to heal inner hurts or fulfil inner needs; but most of us do this to some extent. (We can even be addicted to having addictions!)

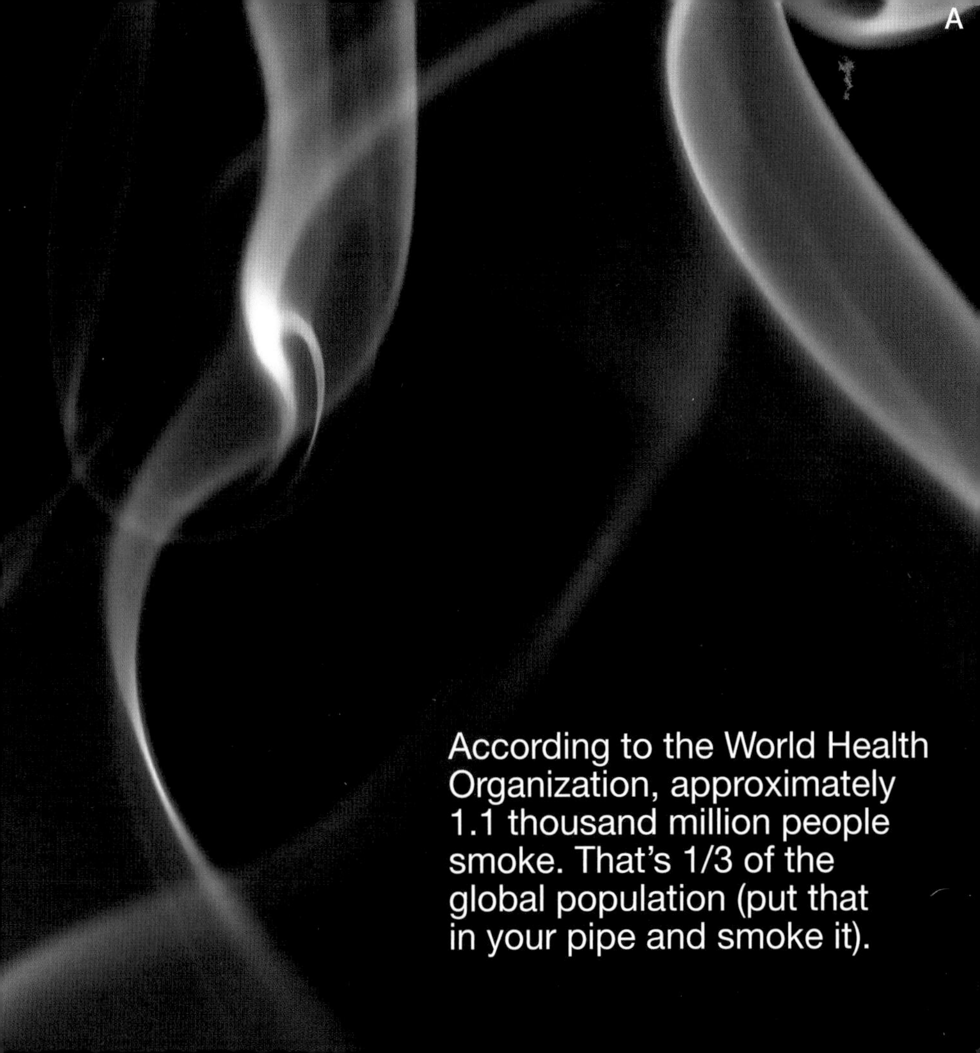
A
According to the World Health Organization, approximately 1.1 thousand million people smoke. That’s 1/3 of the global population (put that in your pipe and smoke it).

A
11
24
16
33
14
31
9

Addiction has varying degrees of severity – some of us are addicted to exercise, chocolate or computer games. Some of us smoke, are addicted to sex, drink excessively or use illegal drugs. Some prescribed medication may also create withdrawal problems (see p.358).

Though challenging, addiction can be overcome.

1) First we have to realise we've a problem and be motivated enough to seek help.
2) If we're addicted to chemical substances, we'll need a detoxification period, time for our bodies to get rid of the drugs or alcohol. Medication is available to reduce the effects of detoxification; withdrawal symptoms can be hard to experience without medical or emotional support.
3) Next, we need to start understanding why we've become addicted. We can learn to talk about our problems, feelings and the challenges we may be experiencing which have led us to drink heavily or take drugs.

Help is available through many UK organisations, some deal with the main types of addiction, some are more specific. Some run treatment centres and some are anonymous organisations that run support groups to help their members stay in recovery.

If you smoke after sex, you're doing it too fast!

A

Attention Deficit Hyperactivity Disorder (ADHD)

Most people associate ADHD with schoolchildren but adults experience it too. ADHD is a condition affecting the part of the brain that controls attention, concentration and impulse.

ADHD affects around 7% of the 7.3 million school-age children in the UK.

Those who experience ADHD behave disruptively, in ways that cannot be explained by other psychiatric or brain function conditions or that are not in keeping with the behaviour of people of their own age or intelligence level.

"You can learn many things from children. How much patience you have, for instance!" Franklin P Jones

People with ADHD find it hard to focus or give their attention to things. They can become hyperactive, experience mood swings or behave impulsively.

"When I approach a child, he inspires in me two sentiments: tenderness for what he is, and respect for what he may become" Louis Pasteur.

Some research suggests ADHD is a genetic condition, it's inherited: if one child in a family has it there's a 30–40% chance that another sibling may experience it, and there's a 45% chance that at least one parent has it too. The behavioural part of our brain develops during childhood through interaction and learning from others, and this could also explain how the condition's passed on.

Some research shows that in a small percentage of cases ADHD is caused by a brain injury during our development – the result of alcohol or tobacco use during pregnancy, or an accidental head injury after birth.

Though it's not entirely associated with social issues, family problems, learned behaviour and excessive TV or video game watching can exacerbate a pre-existing condition.

ADHD can be treated. Experts believe a combination of treatments works well. A child needs a proper diagnosis from a psychiatrist, child psychologist, educational psychologist or child neurologist. Medication can help as well as behavioural therapy and proper support at school.

Each individual child will respond differently, but if the right treatment plan is put into action, a child with ADHD has every chance of achieving their full potential and living a normal healthy life.

"Children are our most valuable resource."
Herbert Hoover

If you think your child has ADHD, talk to their teacher, they and your doctor can put you in touch with someone who can diagnose and treat the condition.

Affirmations

Our mind is programmed before we're eight years old. We're taught by our parents or caregivers how to value ourselves, others and the world around us (whether positively or negatively).

The messages we take in become beliefs; we either believe good things about ourselves or not, depending on what we learned in the first place.

The way we value ourselves and the beliefs we hold will influence how we think, feel and act. We learn to behave in response to our beliefs, and this in time reinforces them. Often these beliefs are in held in our unconscious, so we're unaware of them. So something we're unaware of influences our behaviour (see p.64.

What we learned about life and ourselves as children may no longer apply in adult life.

Using affirmations can help us unlearn early values. They are powerful, positive statements we can say or think to ourselves to help us change negative thinking, develop healthier beliefs and heal hurts from the past.

Affirmations are simple and positive 'I' statements.can be made up of three parts …

1. A statement of what you are or can be. For example: "I am strong" or "I am lovable".

2. A statement of what you could or want be. For example: "I have confidence" or "I am successful".

3. A statement of positive change. For example: "I release the need to smoke fags" (or "disappear into a bottle of red wine as soon as the clocks go back").

The work of Louise Hay and Jean Ilsley Clarke et al. share more information about the power of affirmations and how to use them.

A
The mind is a bit like a garden.
Affirmations can help us develop
new and healthier thoughts
and beliefs that in time can
outgrow the negative ones.
Helpful affirmations (how affirming) have been included in this book.

A

All or nothing thinking

Ever felt like you're on a see-saw – one minute you're up, the next you're down? Everything goes right, then it goes wrong. Up – down – up – down! If this is how you experience life, you might be experiencing all or nothing thinking.

All or nothing thinking, or "splitting", is thought distortion and a defence mechanism. We all experience it from time to time, especially if we've been hurt or feel angry or sad.

All or nothing thinking kicks in when we experience stressful or emotionally charged situations – we say things like "it's the best", "it's the worst", "that's really bad", "you never listen", "it happens every time", "it never works out", "you always do that", "I'm never doing that again". (I never say anything like that!)

Extreme situations can evoke extreme responses. But once we've had time to calm down, our mind can assess things from a wider perspective.

Life experiences and individuals are rarely all good or all bad. (That would be far too simple!)

All or nothing thinking is driven by the deep-held beliefs we learned while small – whether we believe people are untrustworthy or safe, whether we believe we are "good" or "bad".

When our mind sees things in all or nothing terms, it limits our perspective. We're unable to see or consider the options, possibilities or opportunities that have led to a situation or could be gained from it.

Self-exploration can help us understand all or nothing thinking. Using it, we can soon learn new thought processes (and live a bit more the grey – there are many shades of that!).

Affirmation: I can step back from a situation and take my time as I respond.

When our mind see things in all or nothing or black or white terms, it limits our perspective.

Anger

Husband: When I get mad at you, you never fight back. How do you control your anger?

Wife: I clean the toilet bowl.

Husband: How does that help?

Wife: I use your toothbrush!

All too often, anger is a learned response. We react to people or events with anger rather than expressing our genuine feelings of sadness or fear. Our society traditionally considers anger to be far more acceptable than crying or being scared, and some of us still tell our children "don't cry" or "be a brave boy (or girl!)".

At times, anger can be a natural, healthy and authentic feeling. When we're in touch with our anger and can release it appropriately, it's an energy that empowers us.

If we can't express anger effectively, it can become rage – we may become violent or irrational, we may lash out either verbally and physically. If we can't express anger outwardly at all, we may turn it inwards, and this can lead to depression, self-harm or suicide.

Anger is different from rage. If we're in a rage we're out of control, and the rational, thinking part of us has been engulfed by the emotion; our "adult" mind can't apply logic or reason to help us manage the feeling.

But if our anger is authentic it can help us make our position clear; it helps set boundaries between ourselves and others, it lets others know when they've pushed our limits. It can protect us, too.

To "see red" can mean we're angry.

Red is the colour most popular on national flags. But in South Africa red is a sign of mourning.

Within the visible colour spectrum, red has the longest wavelength, so something red appears to be nearer to us than it really is.

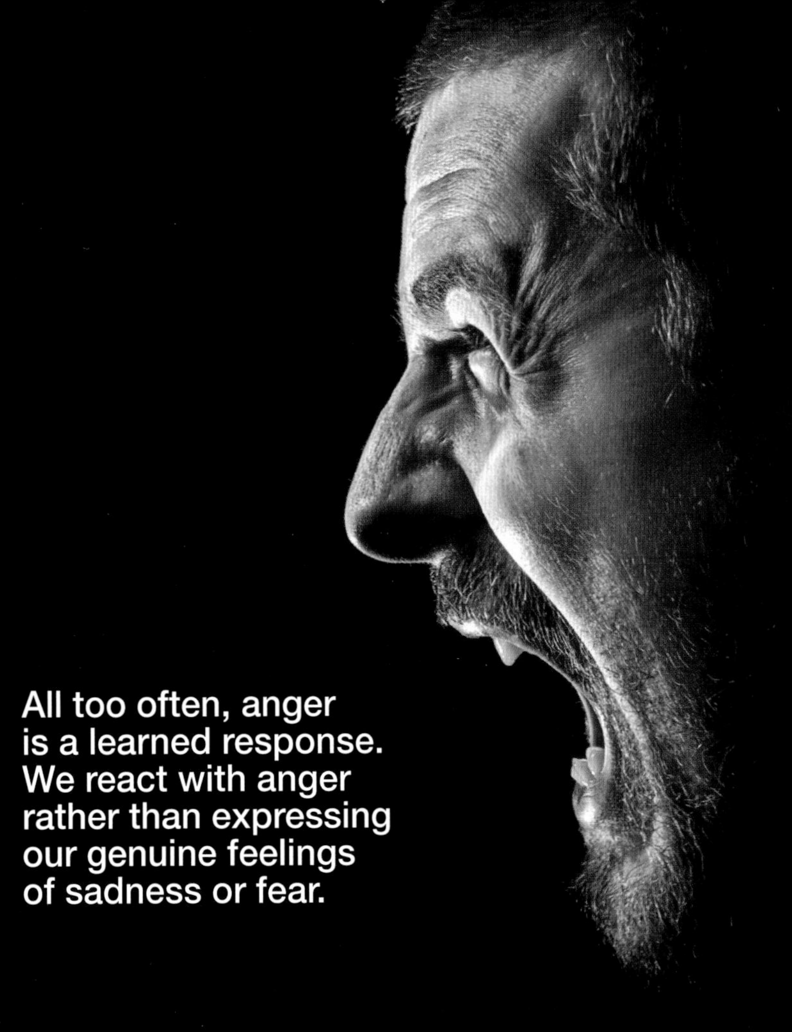

All too often, anger is a learned response. We react with anger rather than expressing our genuine feelings of sadness or fear.

A

Seeing the colour red has a physical effect on us, just looking at it can raise our pulse rate.

When we get angry, the emotional centre of our brain reacts, releasing stress hormones into the body. These chemicals, adrenaline in particular, create a burst of energy – our heartbeat increases, our breath quickens, we might feel fearful, hot or cold, our face might flush or our palms may sweat. That's our body preparing us to fight for our life (or run like hell!).

Anger is helpful if it enables us to solve our problems, but when it exacerbates them our anger is unhealthy. This may also give us a clue as to whether we are really angry or actually sad. Unhealthy anger can affect our body too …

"People who are chronically angry die younger and are six times more likely to die of a heart attack."
www.angermanage.co.uk

When we're angry, sometimes it can be helpful to ask ourselves, "What am I really angry about? Am I really angry, or am I sad or scared?" It's okay to feel those feelings too.

Half of us admit we've reacted to computer problems by hitting our PC, hurling parts of it around, screaming or abusing our colleagues!

If we find it hard to manage anger, we might decide to benefit from anger management courses run through most adult education authorities.

A

The UK has the second-worst road rage record in the world, after South Africa. One in five of us admit to aggressive behaviour (trolley rage!) when shopping and one in twenty of us say we have had a fight with our next door neighbour.

A

"Anybody can become angry, that is easy; but to be angry with the right person, and to the right degree, and at the right time, and for the right purpose, and in the right way, that is not within everybody's power, that is not easy." Aristotle.

Affirmation: It's okay to feel angry, I can express my anger in a non-hurtful way.

Anorexia nervosa

In the UK today, Beat estimate that anorexia nervosa will affect 1 in 200 women and 1 in 2000 men at some point in their lives.

The first written acknowledgment of anorexia nervosa, by physician and minister John Reynolds, dates back to 1669. It was recognised as a clinical condition in 1873.

Anorexia nervosa literally means loss of appetite for nervous reasons; the Greek prefix "an" means "without" and "orexis" means appetite. However, the definition is misleading...

Because if we experience anorexia nervosa, we lose the ability to allow ourselves to satisfy our appetite. We restrict what we eat and drink, and we can become obsessed with burning off calories. Food becomes the focus of how we cope or take control of life rather than an attempt at starvation.

If we have anorexia nervosa it's a way of demonstrating our independence through controlling what we eat and drink. It can be difficult for others to understand that although food is an important issue, anorexia nervosa is really about feelings.

"Control is never achieved when sought after directly. It is the surprising outcome of letting go." James Arthur Ray

With anorexia nervosa we experience extreme weight loss; we may get constipated, have abdominal pains and feel dizzy or faint a lot. Our tummies may bloat or our bones can weaken, or we might get a puffy face or ankles. We may lose our hair or feel cold all the time. Our skin may become dry, rough and discoloured. As females our periods can stop (we certainly don't fancy sex!), and long-term anorexia can affect our fertility, making it hard to conceive.

Anorexia nervosa affects the way we think, too. We fear putting on weight or we become obsessed with what others are eating. We're unable to see ourselves as we are – we think we're overweight and unattractive, and we can't enjoy and celebrate our bodies just as they are.

We may experience mood swings or hear a voice inside that challenges our views on eating and exercise. We may have denial – where we can't see we've got a problem.

Anorexia nervosa can affect our behaviour as well; we might do obsessive things with food, choose to wear baggy clothes to hide our bodies, even vomit or want to take laxatives.

Anorexia nervosa can be overcome. It may take time and effort, but it's perfectly possible to feel differently about ourselves and begin to enjoy our food and celebrate our body.

First we have to realise we've a problem, be motivated to get help and most of all believe we can get better.

"To wish to be well is part of becoming well"
Seneca

Antidepressants

Antidepressants carry a load of stigmas, so let's get one thing straight: there's nothing inadequate or shameful about taking them. At times we may need them to help get us back on our feet as we begin on our path of healing.

In 2007, 30 million anti-depressant prescriptions were prescribed in the UK.

Antidepressants work by changing the chemical levels in our brain. The chemicals that control our mood are monoamines, they're neurotransmitters. These chemicals carry electrical messages around our brain. If we've got the right balance of these chemicals we feel okay (but if we haven't, the lights may be on but we don't feel at home!).

Antidepressants are not a cure, but they can help us short term. For some, other treatments such as the "talking cure", can be more beneficial in treating depression longer term (see p116).

There are many types of antidepressants, as with any medication it's important to talk to your doctor and always read the label or information given with your medication. In here there's information about:

1 Tricyclic antidepressants (TCAs), the oldest type (see p.37)

2 Selective serotonin re-uptake inhibitors (SSRIs) and selective serotonin and norepineprine re-uptake inhibitors (SSNRIs) (see p.38).

3 Monoamine oxidase inhibitors (MAOIs) (see p.39).

Antidepressants are not tranquillisers, nor are they said to be addictive, though some of us may feel we rely on them to get by. If we're taking antidepressants, we need to monitor how we feel.

Medication affects each of us in different ways, and the way we respond gives our doctor information as to how effective they are or whether we're on the right dose.

TCAs (tricyclic antidepressants)

TCAs were the first type of antidepressants. SSRIs are more common today because they have fewer side effects, but TCAs are still helpful, especially for treating panic attacks.

TCAs work by blocking the brain's ability to "re-uptake" serotonin and norepinephrine. These chemicals regulate our mood. When TCAs block the brain's re-uptake of them, they become more concentrated in the synapses – the spaces between our brain's nerve cells.

TCAs can be effective in treating insomnia and, unlike SSRIs, they don't affect our sex drive or function (hooray!).

Like other antidepressants, TCAs can take a few weeks to start working; we may start off on a low dose, which can be increased depending on how our brain responds. Talk to your doctor and see how you feel.

SSRIs and SSNRIs

SSRIs work on our serotonin levels. If we experience too much stress for a long period of time our serotonin levels can drop. SSRIs boost them back up again.

SSRIs should only be taken if prescribed by a doctor. Like a lot of antidepressants, they need to be taken for a long period of time. Our dose will depend on how we respond to them; we may need to monitor how we feel and feedback to our doctor. Lots of people take a relatively low dose of SSRIs for a while just to get back on track.

SSRIs can take a couple of weeks to kick in and we may experience side effects. We can even feel worse to begin with this is because the medication is changing our brain chemical levels. At first, we might get the shakes or feel anxious. We may experience drowsiness or sweaty palms (my palms were like Niagara Falls when I started taking them!). We may even feel constipated, sick or vomit.

SSRIs can affect our sex drive. We might go off sex or find it hard to have orgasms (don’t panic - it doesn’t last forever!).

SSNRIs are the newest types of antidepressants, they work to slow our brains reuptake of serotonin and norepinephrine. SSNRIs have many similarities to SSRIs. They too may take a while to start working.

SSNRI Side effects can include headaches, anxiety, nausea, indigestion, constipation, shaking, muscle twitching or an increase in our heart rate.

As with all medication, talk to your doctor or psychiatrist and keep an eye on how you and your body are responding to them.

MAOIs (monoamine oxidase inhibitors)

MAOIs aren't prescribed as frequently as SSRIs or TCAs. If we find that SSRIs or TCAs aren't helping with the problem, then we can, with medical supervision, try MAOIs. Especially if we're experiencing social anxiety, agoraphobia, panic attacks or borderline personality disorders, MAOIs can be really helpful.

MAOIs work by raising our monoamine levels. Monoamines are chemicals like serotonin, dopamine and noradrenaline, which help us feel good. These chemicals get released in the brain and then they normally get broken down by an enzyme (another chemical) called monoamine oxidase.

But MAOIs stop the monoamine oxidase from breaking down monoamines, so their levels increase, and we have more of them in our brains for longer, which helps to make us feel better.

MAOIs, like other antidepressants, take time to work, so a talk with the doctor is essential.

If we take MAOIs we need to be on a special diet; we must avoid foods that contain high levels of the amino acid tyramine, as this can cause a dangerous rise in blood pressure.

We can still eat chocolate – phew! – but items such as cheese, pickled herrings, broad bean pods, fermented soya bean extract, and yeast extract – i.e. Bovril, Oxo, Marmite and most alcoholic or low-alcohol drinks – are a no-no. Cough mixture, too, reacts badly with MAOI medication.

A

Antipsychotics

Antipsychotics or neuroleptic drugs have been used since the 1950s. They're generally used to treat psychosis, schizophrenia, bipolar disorder, mania and sometimes delusions. They can also treat nausea or balance problems; they even help people with persistent hiccups (which would drive me mad!).

There are two types: typical antipsychotics or first generation, and atypical or second generation (sounds a bit like Star Trek!). Both work by blocking dopamine pathways in the brain.

Dopamine is the brain chemical most associated with experiencing pleasure: it's released when we enjoy good food or sex. It affects the way we perceive things, our mood, how we learn and how we sleep and concentrate. But if too much dopamine is released we may experience psychosis...

And that's when we may be prescribed an antipsychotic.

Clozapine, is an atypical antipsychotic which also stands on it's own. Though we have to have blood tests to take it, which often puts us off, it can be a very affective form of treatment and has revolutionised some peoples lives.

Side effects of antipsychotics include stiff muscles or tremors, a dry mouth or over-salivation, restlessness and loss of movement or muscle spasms.

Some affect our prolactin levels, a male and female hormone. In women this can lead to breast growth or a drop in our sex drive, or our periods may stop.

In men it can cause impotence or ejaculation problems. Sometimes, though rare, men can experience a constant erection which should be treated as an emergency.

Antipsychotics can also cause sleepiness, blurred vision,weight gain, constipation and irregularities in heart rhythm – we all respond differently. They are not a cure, but they do help relieve symptoms. Talk to your doctor or psychiatrist.

Our dopamine level affects the way we perceive things, our mood, how we learn and attend to things.

Anxiety

"Love looks forward, hate looks back, anxiety has eyes all over its head."
Mignon McLaughlin

The word "anxiety" originates from the Latin word "angere" meaning to choke, press together or torment. The feeling of anxiety originates from the beginning of mankind!

Anxiety in its purest form is fear, diluted fear. It's part of our flight/fight/freeze mechanism, an involuntary response system that gets us ready for action or escape (see p.154).

From butterflies in our stomachs to that horrible stone-like feeling of dread, we've all experienced anxiety in some form or another – that uneasy feeling before taking exams, driving tests or job interviews (or for some, worse still, waiting for the results for any of the above!).

But anxiety, in healthy amounts, is useful to us. It warns us, it reminds us to take care of ourselves, it's our body signalling danger and telling us to be careful.

Anxiety keeps us sharp; it heightens our awareness, and it can help our performance in some situations. We may notice our anxiety levels increase if a situation isn't right, so we can act accordingly and as our anxiety subsides we feel more safe and secure.

The word "secure" comes from two small Latin words: "se" meaning without and "cure" meaning care – being without care – freedom from anxiety.

For some of us anxiety never subsides; we feel uneasy, apprehensive, tense and worried most of the time, but for no apparent reason. This is when we may need help.

A
Anxiety disorders affect
5% of the UK population.

Prolonged anxiety can affect our body. Some research shows it increases our chances of getting heart disease. It can affect the strength of our immune system too – that's the part of us that helps us fight diseases, from the common cold to cancer.

Too much anxiety can also lead to phobias, obsessive-compulsive disorder and panic attacks.

Anxiety can be treated (well that's one less thing to worry about). A doctor or psychiatrist can prescribe medication, though many sufferers find talking to a counsellor helps too.

Getting to the root of our anxiety is what helps to cure it.

"Nothing diminishes anxiety faster than action." Walter Anderson

Some of our anxiety may be caused by our situation or by longer-term problems at work or at home. We may need to make some changes to our job or relationships. Anxiety can also arise because of the past: we may find that we have some difficult early experiences or painful memories we need to work through, and that's when it can be sensible to consult a counsellor.

"Real difficulties can be overcome, it is only the imaginary ones that are unconquerable." Theodore N. Vail

All kinds of "talking therapies" can help us explore and overcome our anxiety; art therapy is just one of them (see p. 47).

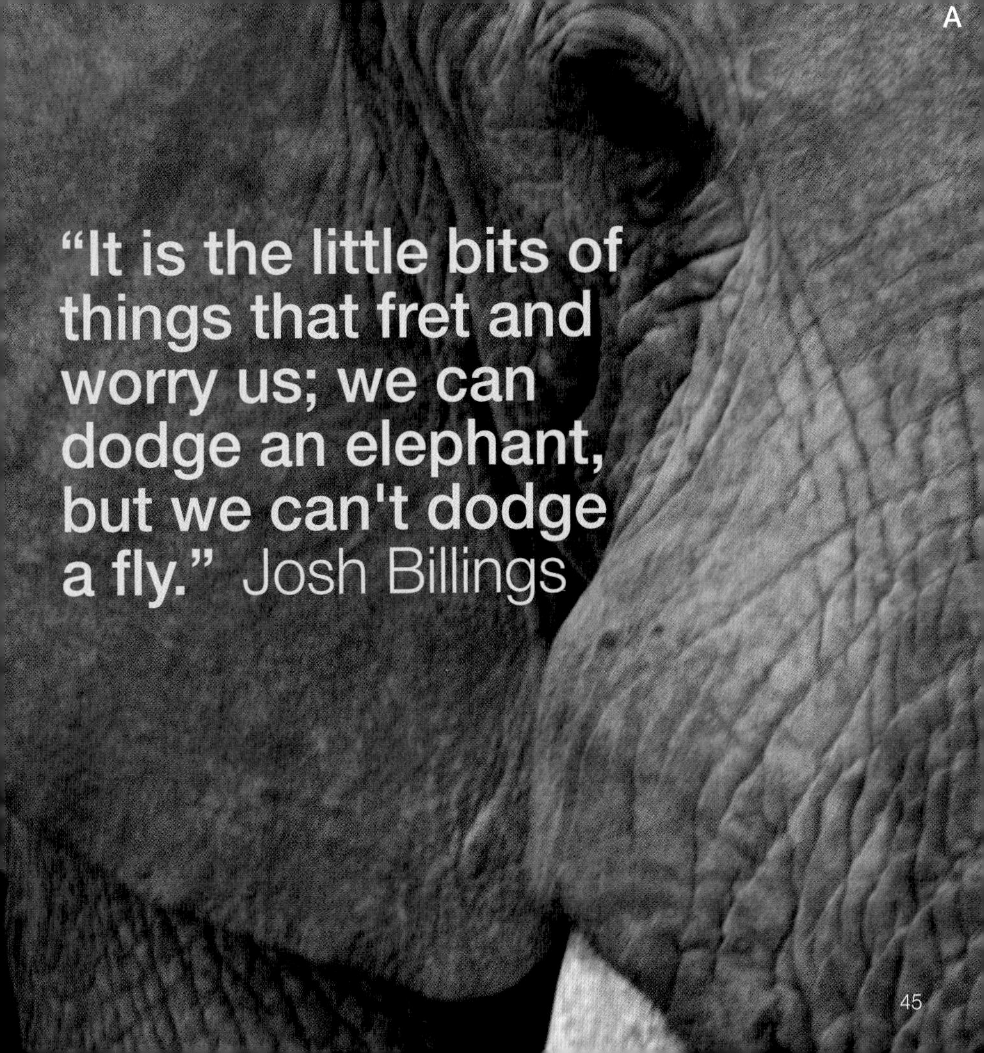
A
"It is the little bits of things that fret and worry us; we can dodge an elephant, but we can't dodge a fly." Josh Billings

A

Art therapy

"Doctor, Doctor, I can't stop painting myself gold…"

"…Don't worry, it's just a gilt complex!"

Art therapy is a form of psychotherapy that uses artistic materials – paint, chalks, pens or clay – as tools of expression. Art therapy combines the theories and approaches of psychotherapy with the psychological understanding of the creative process.

Art therapists use artistic materials and creative processes to help us explore and express issues, feelings and experiences we're finding it difficult to come to terms with.

Art therapy became an important form of therapy after the Second World War. Some of those who had survived atrocities in WWII found creative expression a helpful way to overcome the traumatic things they had experienced. It's a way to explore and release emotions.

Art is non-verbal communication and can reveal deeper emotions or insights.

Art therapy can be especially helpful for children or young adults, and those of us who aren't yet able to fully express ourselves with words.

It's okay, you don't have to be Van Gogh to see an art therapist but if it sounds like it's something for you, all art therapists should be registered with the British Association of Art Therapists.

Assertivenes

The word "NO" is a complete sentence!

Assertiveness is important; it helps us look after our mind and well being. True assertiveness is about recognising and meeting our own needs at the same time as respecting those of other people. It's not about controlling others.

When we're assertive we're able to communicate directly and honestly; we can express our feelings, needs, opinions and rights without violating, hurting or disrespecting others.

When we're assertive, we feel good about ourselves. We can get more out of life because we can ask openly and directly for what we want or need, or calmly reject what we don't.

Non-assertiveness (submissiveness) is when we allow others to violate our rights or disregard our needs, feelings and opinions.

If we're submissive, we tend to feel as though we are not as important as other people. If we are submissive in a situation, we can end up feeling hurt, angry, anxious or disappointed with ourselves.

There are 4 types of assertiveness:

1. **Basic assertion:** a simple straightforward expression of our needs, opinions or beliefs, We use statements like "I want", "I need" and "I feel".
2. **Empathetic assertion:** a way of expressing our own situation, feelings or needs while acknowledging someone else's – "I know you've been working really hard recently, but I'd like us to spend some time together, because our relationship is important to me."
3. **Escalating assertion:** a form of assertion that works in a situation where our rights are being continually violated or ignored.

We can gradually escalate our assertion and firmness by mentioning (not threatening) the resulting action we'll take if our needs aren't met. "I'm feeling overwhelmed by my workload at the moment. If you continue to ask me to take on more responsibilities I may have to go and discuss my situation with the personnel department." (That'll stop em!)

4. **I-language or I statements**: This is a way of expressing negative experiences and involves three statements and a question (all calmly and pleasantly, though firmly, expressed!):

When you do…(insert other persons behaviour) I feel (insert your experience). So what I'd like is (what you want instead). Are you willing to do that?

So we can say something like, "When you make a mess where I've just cleaned up, I feel angry. I want you to clean up after yourself; will you do that?" (Politely hand them the dish cloth, stand back and watch 'em clean).

Some of us are more assertive than others; it's not something we're born with, but with support and practice it's something we learn.

Evening classes and assertiveness courses are available all over the UK.

Affirmation: My needs are important.

Assumption

(Yeah…I know the meaning of this one) When we ASSUME we make an ASS out of U and ME!

“Some people become so expert at reading between the lines they don’t read the lines.” Margaret Millar

We assume things all the time – 90% of our memory is “construct” rather than recall.

“Construct” means that our mind jumps to conclusions that match our beliefs; we assume what’s happening rather than checking things out. When we assume, our mind makes decisions about situations, people or even ourselves before we’ve actually researched or explored them.

Because of the way our mind is programmed, we assume different things in different situations.

“The amazing thing is, the "assumption" part of our decision-making process is usually the part that gets the least examination...it's the part we take for granted.” Christian Overman

We assume we won’t get the job we want, so we don’t apply; we assume someone is heterosexual when they might be gay; we assume someone won’t like us before we’ve said hello.

Humans assumed the world was flat until we got round to exploring it!

It’s worth exploring the assumptions we make, the things we take for granted or assume about people.

Exploring our assumptions can open our mind. Assume nothing and uncover everything!

Affirmation: It’s okay to ask questions and check out my world

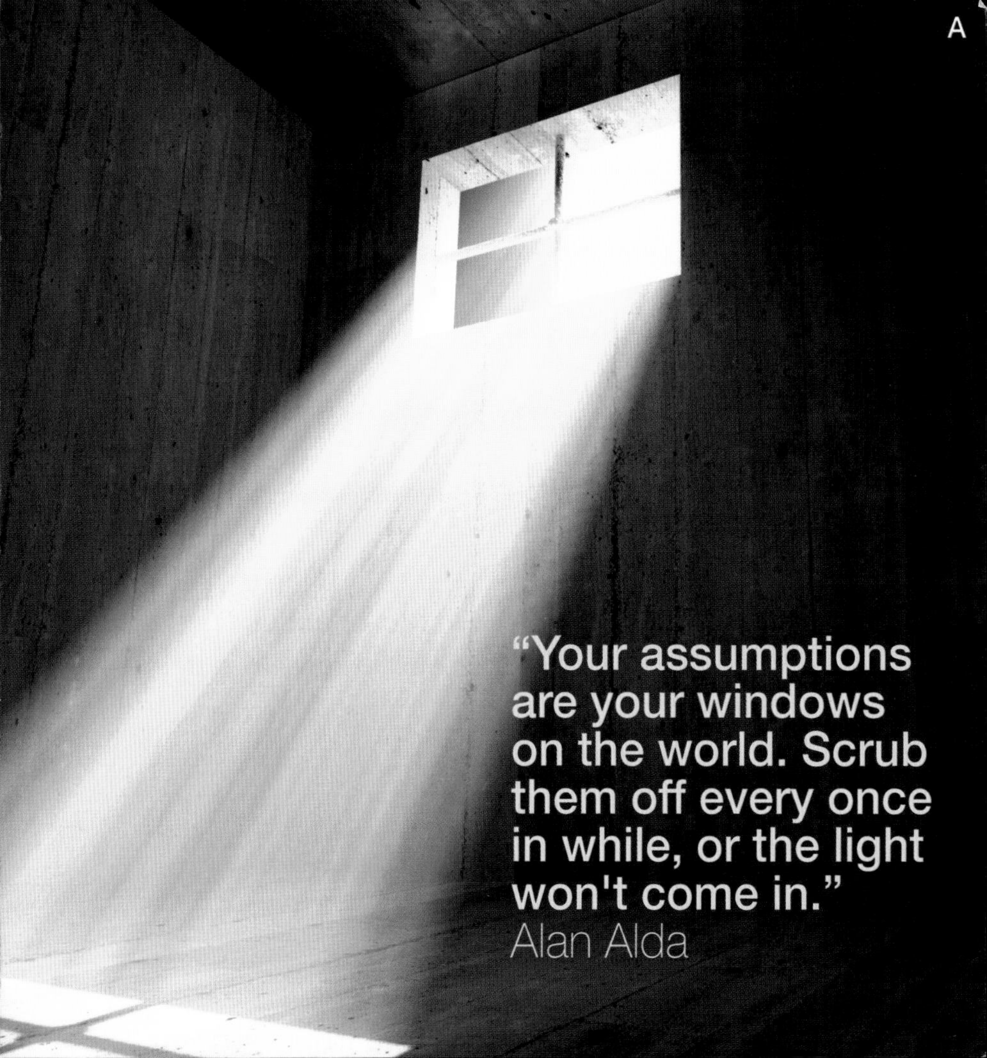
A
“Your assumptions
are your windows
on the world. Scrub
them off every once
in while, or the light
won't come in.”
Alan Alda

Authentic feelings

Sadness, happiness, fear and, sometimes, anger are our core, authentic feelings. They're feelings we experience in the moment, just as they arise (well at least until they're judged or censored by our mind).

In early life, while our mind was developing, most of us learned how and what to feel. The adults around us might have taught us that some feelings were okay but others were not – to feel happy was "good", to feel fear was "bad", to cry was "bad", to feel angry was "naughty"!

Negatively or positively, our early lessons in "feeling" can affect us later. If we weren't allowed to feel sad as kids we may bottle it up as adults. If we weren't allowed to feel fear it can be hard to be vulnerable or be guided by our anxiety later on.

Our authentic feelings are essential to who we are.

They're unique to each of us and can't be argued with. Authentic feelings help form our sense of reality and help us assess our needs in life.

If we feel angry we may need to walk away, and if we feel sad we may need a cuddle – but if we can't feel our feelings, our needs can't be met.

We often hide our authentic feelings – we think others won't like us if we tell them we're angry, or we don't share our sadness because we fear rejection.

Our authentic feelings are important to us.

The more we're in touch with our own true feelings, the more we can openly relate to others, and doing this is an important part of a healthy mind.

Our feelings inform us. When they are authentic, our feelings are part of our individual, natural and autonomous state...

"Our feelings are our most genuine paths to knowledge."
Audre Lorde

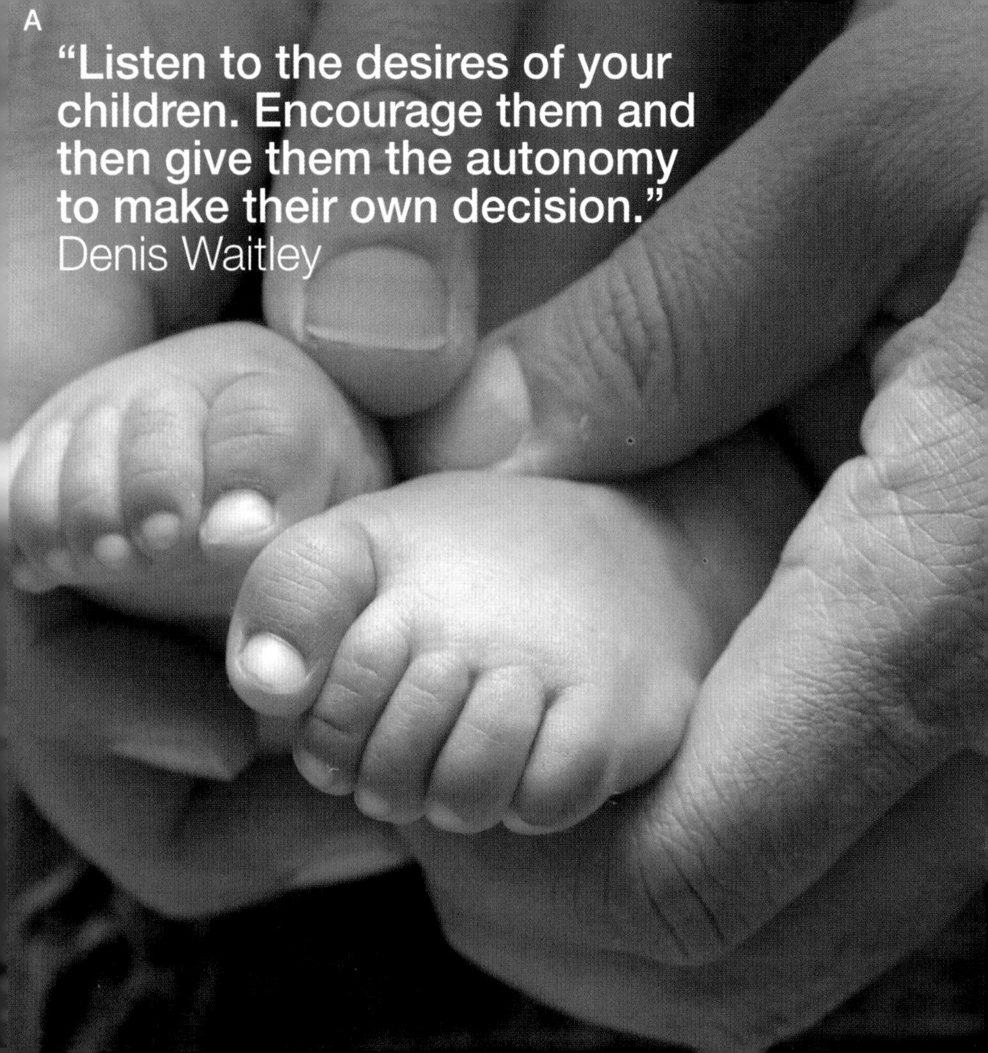
A
“Listen to the desires of your children. Encourage them and then give them the autonomy to make their own decision.”
Denis Waitley

Autonomy

The word "autonomy" is Greek in origin; it means to give law to one's self, to live within one's own rules and values. According to Eric Berne (1964), we attain our autonomy when we "release or recover … three capacities: awareness, spontaneity and intimacy".

Awareness is about seeing things as we really see them rather than how we were taught to see them. Awareness belongs in the present moment, being in the here and now in both mind and body (see p.56).

Spontaneity means choice and freedom. We're all free to feel all our feelings, and we can learn to express ourselves just as we are. The more spontaneous we are, the more intimate we can be; we don't have to hide or play games with others.

Intimacy is about honest communication (see p. 204).

As aware, spontaneous, intimate people we can share our feelings and exist in the here and now.

Without realising it, our parents and caregivers teach us how to experience things. We learn from them how to think, how to feel and how to behave towards ourselves and others.

We all start off as autonomous beings, but our contact with adults affects the growth of our mind. Their words and teachings apply layers to our being that in time colour and condition our own natural state. Rather than responding to life from our own sense of self, most of us are conditioned to experience things as others taught us to.

Our natural state is at the core of our being. Deep down inside we know what's right for us. The more we exist in our natural state, the easier it is to be true to ourselves.

We can experience more happiness and contentment as we act in accordance with our natural experience.

Awareness

Our conscious mind and body sensations provide us with our awareness. Our unconscious mind is outside of awareness, but as we explore it we can become more aware. Awareness is about being in the here and now – our mind and body are connected and present, and we've got no memories from the past or fears of the future.

Being aware both in mind and in body can help improve our state in life. When aware of ourselves we're in touch with our body and the way we feel, and we're aware of our thinking and what we're doing.

In this "present" state we have more control, and we can choose what to do rather than just react unthinkingly to things that happen to us.

Awareness is about noticing and observing our state in the moment, separating past patterns from present opportunities.

Rather than responding with a knee-jerk reaction, we can step back and assess before we engage (we all could do with that from time to time).

The more awareness we have about our mind and our thinking, the more choices we can make to change what we do. If we're aware of patterns or problems in life, we can take action to change, grow and get better.

The present moment is where we're most alive; we're not scouring over the past or worrying about the future. As we become more aware of who we are, we can strengthen our sense of individuality and autonomy.

We all bring old baggage to new situations, but the more we're aware of our issues or hangups, the less they affect us as new things happen.

Affirmation: I have the power to change at any moment.

"The first step toward change is awareness. The second step is acceptance." Nathaniel Branden

Behaviour

Behaviour refers to the actions, reactions and things we "do" in response to our feelings or experiences.Most of our behaviour is either learned or copied.

"All human actions have one or more of these seven causes: chance, nature, compulsions, habit, reason, passion and desire." Aristotle

Behaviour can be biologically driven, instinctive – we respond to feeling hungry or thirsty or take action to avoid danger or life threatening situations.

Behaviour can be conscious or unconscious; we can be aware we're doing something or not, as the case may be.

Behaviour is influenced by our attitudes, values and feelings as well as the culture or society we live in. And most of all, behaviour is learned and can be unlearned (phew!).

"In essence, if we want to direct our lives, we must take control of our consistent actions. It's not what we do once in a while that shapes our lives, but what we do consistently." Antony Robbins

Before we learn to speak, we learn or copy behaviour. We learn to behave through association; if we behave in an acceptable/appropriate/desirable way we get rewarded – we get fed, cuddled or praised.

But if we behave in an unacceptable/inappropriate/undesirable way we get reprimanded, told off, smacked, ignored, sent to our room or isolated on the naughty step (it's all on someone else's terms though).

B
"Behavior is a mirror in which every one displays his image."
Johann Wolfgang von Goethe

So as we grow, we learn behaviour has consequences; these positive or negative experiences depend on how we behave. Then the consequences we experience reinforce our behaviour.

Some of the behaviour we learnt as kids follows us into adulthood (some things never change).

Most of the time if we behave “appropriately” we can get what we want, but sometimes old behaviour gets in the way – we behave aggressively towards our colleagues or partners when we could have talked through a situation calmly; we smoke and can’t get out of the habit.

Sometimes we don’t behave at all and we just avoid situations when we’d rather do something.

If our behaviour stops us from getting what we want or causes us or others distress, it might be time to do some unlearning!

We can explore and develop our behavioural choices by talking to a therapist or counsellor.

Affirmation: I can explore and choose new ways of behaving to get my needs met.

"Remember, people will judge you by your actions, not your intentions. You may have a heart of gold but so does a hard-boiled egg!"
Anon

Being

"Being" has several meanings, but fundamentally the word means that which exists or has life. Being is a state, a state of existence, and a state of life.

How many of us are human beings as opposed to humans doing?

When we feel we're in our being state – whether we're feeling sad or happy – we're capable of thinking, doing and being.

When we are in our being state, we're in the moment, in touch with all of our senses, aware.

Ever had those moments when you just lose yourself in something? Weeding a flower bed, walking, looking out to sea, singing, listening to music, meditating? – Times when we just are, we're in the moment and feel at one with life? That's being.

These days, "being" is one of the most challenging human states for us to experience – how ironic, given that we are called human beings!

Medication can't get us there but dedication, meditation and breathing exercises can help us develop our state of being!

Affirmation: I have all the time to be all that I am and can be.

"We are so obsessed with doing that we have no time and no imagination left for being… As a result, men are valued not for what they are but for what they do or what they have for their usefulness."

Thomas Merton

Beliefs

"Man is what he believes."
Anton Chekhov

Our beliefs are important to our state of mind.

Inside most of us is a set of core beliefs, formed in early childhood and based on our experiences and decisions made back then. But when we're adults, our beliefs are those that we have been taught as children, and are often inappropriate for our current situation.

Our belief system not only creates what we believe about ourselves but what we believe about others and life.

Our beliefs influence how we see ourselves, others and the world around us. They influence how we feel, what we're capable of and what life can offer us.

Core beliefs are powerful: they influence our thoughts, and thus our feelings and actions.

If our core beliefs are that we're unlovable, a failure or unworthy, this will influence how we see ourselves, how we think others see us and what we can achieve; this set of beliefs seems to be widespread throughout our Western culture. But if our core beliefs are that we are lovable, worthy and that life is fun then we are likely to experience all of that too.

Because our belief system is based on our childhood experiences, our beliefs are often outdated. As we grow our experiences in life can change our beliefs. We no longer believe in Santa Claus or the Tooth Fairy – so why should we still believe we are unlovable or unworthy?

Our beliefs are familiar, and familiarity feels much safer than the unknown. But if what's familiar doesn't seem to work, we may need to examine our beliefs. Do we believe we deserve success – do we feel we can change and do better? If we're aware of our deeply held beliefs it's a little easier to change them

“The mind is like a parachute; it works much better when it's open!” Anon

“To accomplish great things we must not only act, but also dream; not only plan, but also believe.”
Anatole France

Believing

Believing is important.

If we believe in something we can make it happen.

When we believe, it gives us hope, energy and motivation.

When we believe we can do something we tend to think, feel and behave as if it's possible.

At some times in our life it might be worth exploring our beliefs.

By using affirmations we can train our mind to see things differently (see p.24).

If we believe we'll do well, our mind can support us, if we believe we won't, it works the same way.

Sometimes we have to get our head around our head!

"If you believe you can, you probably can. If you believe you won't, you most assuredly won't. Belief is the ignition switch that gets you off the launching pad."
Denis Waitley

Benzodiazepines

Why does the pharmacist talk quietly?

She doesn't want to wake the sleeping tablets!

Benzodiazepines have been available since the 1960s. They're tranquillizers, and they slow down some of the thought processes in our mind, to help us feel calm, relaxed, even drowsy.

Benzodiazepines are used to treat some types of anxiety disorders, but are generally used as sleeping tablets.

Benzodiazepines affect the brain chemical known as gamma-aminobutyric acid (GABA to save typos!).

GABA stops the neurons, the electrical transmitters in our brains, from communicating with each other, and this slows our brain down.

Benzodiazepines help GABA to work even harder, and this slows the brain down even more, so we feel calmer, less afraid and less tense. That's why they help us sleep – but they can also help people who experience anxiety.

Benzodiazepine drugs include nitrazepam, flurazepam, loprazolam, lormetazepam, temazepam and diazepam (lots of pams aren't there?).

Nitrazepam and flurazepam are long-acting sleeping pills that may have side effects which feel like a hangover the next day.

Loprazolam and lormetazepam and temazepam are short-acting, producing little or no hangover but sometimes producing withdrawal symptoms.

The most common side effects of taking benzodiazepines are feelings of drowsiness or light-headedness the next day. Some of us may feel confused, forgetful or unsteady when taking them.

Others of us experience headaches, vertigo, tremors, muscle or joint ache or changes in our sex drive.

At times it's possible to experience paradoxical effects – instead of feeling calmer when taking benzodiazepines, we end up feeling more excited, and our behaviour changes can range from being talkative to becoming aggressive or antisocial.

Benzodiazepines are prescribed medication and should be used with caution, especially if we have asthma, bronchitis, weak muscles or a history of drug or alcohol abuse.

Sometimes it's hard to withdraw from this kind of medication; we can become dependent on it.

They're addictive drugs, so should be used with caution. If you're likely to be prescribed them, check carefully with your doctor or psychiatrist.

Bipolar affective disorder

Bipolar affective disorder used to be called manic depression. It's a condition that affects 1% of the UK population. Bipolar is an imbalance in the part of the brain that regulates mood; it's a condition where we experience episodes of mania and episodes of depression.

These episodes involve feeling high or elated, or low and lethargic. It's not like everyday ups and downs; these feelings tend to last for longer periods, but we can also experience normal mood levels too (thank goodness for that!).

What causes bipolar disorder isn't fully understood, but it appears to run in families. It's quite common: 1 in 100 people are diagnosed with bipolar which can occur at any time, but is mostly diagnosed amongst 18-24 year-olds.

> Some evidence suggests that there is a link between bipolar disorder and creative people. Many well known actors, artists, comedians, musicians and writers experience the condition (so do I).

Thomas A Harris (1967) suggests that manic depression is experienced if the "adult" part of us (which developed during early childhood) was "shut out" and unable to grow and develop.

He believed that if recognition from parents or caregivers while we were young was inconsistent, overbearing, contradictory and extreme, our mind didn't learn that there are lots of experiences to be had in between.

If we learned to believe that life or even ourselves are either really good or really bad, we can end up feeling "life is rich" or "life is empty" later on. If we think in this way, whether aware of it or not, it will have an affect on our mood.

Bipolar disorder affects each individual differently and is very treatable. Some of us may need medication to help ease our symptoms, others of us may find the talking therapies helpful, it depends how acute our experiences are.

Medication can help balance the brain chemicals that manage our mood and counselling or psychotherapy can provide on going support, ways to develop healthier thought patters or coping strategies.

B

Body Dysmorphic Disorder (BDD)

Around 1% of the UK population experience BDD.

In 1886, the Italian physician Dr Morselli came up with the word "dysmorphophobia" to name what we know today as Body Dysmorphic Disorder. Dysmorphophobia comes from the Greek word "dysmorph" which means "mis-shapen".

BDD is a mind disorder where we become preoccupied with a defect that we perceive in our appearance – even though it's something that others don't see as important, or they hardly even notice. To be diagnosed with BDD, our preoccupation must cause us significant distress or handicap.

Sigmund Freud had a client he called The Wolf Man. This guy believed his nose was so misshapen that he couldn't work or go out in public (just goes to show how powerful our beliefs about ourselves are).

Although BDD is under-researched, some studies have shown that it usually starts in adolescence. It's a treatable condition, there is evidence to suggest that in particular cognitive behavioural therapy is helpful and anti-obsessional medication can also benefit those who experience BDD.

What we believe about our body will affect how we feel, think and behave towards it. Our self-image is important to us; we're taught how to value our body by parents and caregivers while we are young. Those early beliefs can affect us, for good or ill, later on in life.

If we experience difficulty in liking, accepting and enjoying our body just as it is, it might be worth exploring what we learned or we were taught about the way we look or how we should appear.

Affirmation: I accept and love my body. I am wonderful as I am.

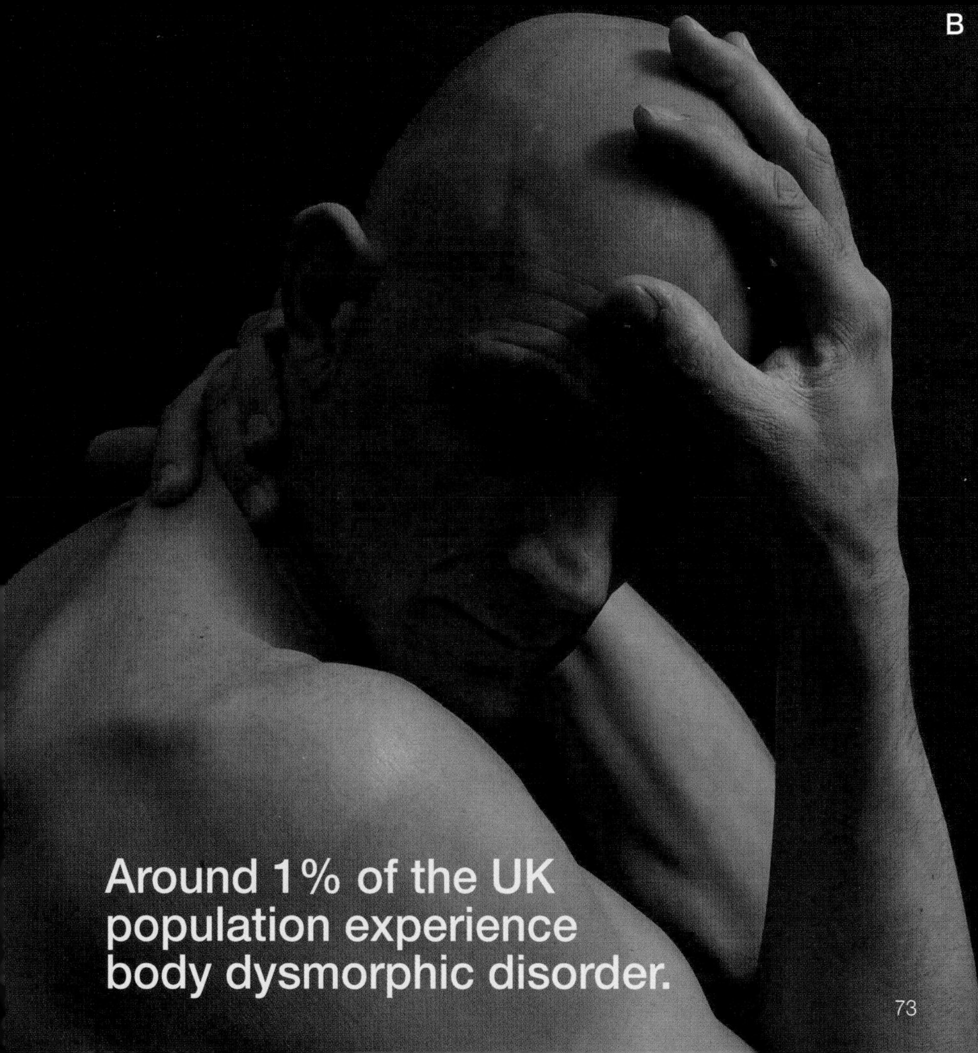
Around 1% of the UK
population experience
body dysmorphic disorder.

B

The body

Our body, like our mind, is utterly amazing!

Our body is run by our mind and tells our mind things, and then responds to our mind in turn. If our mind is stressed our body gets tense, and if our mind is calm our body can soften. The mind and body are intrinsically linked.

Our body and how we take care of it affects our mind: what we eat and drink and how we connect to our body all play a part in how we think and feel.

Some of us don't feel good about our bodies. We're bombarded by magazine and media images (which are either airbrushed, enhanced or stretched!), telling us our bodies should all look the same (how boring).

It can take time to learn to love the skin we're in and accept and enjoy what we've got as our own.

Our bodies are our homes. We learned whilst we were young how to value our body.

If we were told we were beautiful, that's what we'll see. If we think we're attractive then we will be, but if we think that we're not then how can we shine?

We can all learn to love, accept and care for our body. It's part of loving and caring for ourselves.

The mind and body are connected; how we think influences how we feel, and as we learn to think differently about our form it can change how we feel about ourselves inside.

If we feel good we look good … go on, you know you're worth it!

"Begin to see yourself as a soul with a body rather than a body with a soul." Wayne Dyer

B

Body language

It is estimated that body language accounts for 90% of our conversation. Though while an eye roll, smile or nod of the head can convey much more than words, it can sometimes go unnoticed.

Many sorts of body language are understood internationally, but be careful … in Greece (and I don't mean the musical), a nod of the head means no and a shake means yes!

Body language is physical communication. The way we move, stand or use gestures or facial expressions, the way we dress and the way we smell are all part of how and what we say.

We can tell a lot about someone by how they stand or sit. Our faces express how we truly feel, especially the look in our eyes.

Our body language is both conscious and unconscious. Sometimes we're aware of how we move as we speak, and sometimes we're not.

Our unconscious body language says more than we realise. If someone is lying to us their eyes may dart around, and they may hide their palms or shift from one foot to another.

If someone is attracted to us they may touch their bodies as they communicate, unconsciously drawing attention to themselves physically. (Understanding body language is quite useful at times like that!)

By understanding how our bodies “talk” and how we convey messages physically, we can improve the way we communicate. Knowing how to use our body in an interview or on a date is really helpful:

- Stand or sit up straight. If we stand tall and proud, we’ll begin to think and feel that way.
- Make good eye contact – we’ve nothing to hide, it communicates trust and confidence.
- Sit or stand still rather than fidgeting – it communicates composure and confidence.
- Speak slowly and calmly – take time; it shows we’re measured, considered and thoughtful – and it helps to calm us too.
- Use hand gestures – if we need to use our hands to express as we speak we can, it demonstrates enthusiasm. Passion and excitement are infectious.
- Use touch – touch is important. It’s okay to gently and appropriately touch other people – a friendly handshake demonstrates confidence, and a hug expresses care and support.

"Everyone's got a heart. Find a way to touch it!"
Ewen Lewis

The more we’re aware and in touch with our body, the more it can support and express who we are.

Movement and breath can release our emotions, giving our mind confidence, calmness, belief and composure, and touch soothes, and connects us with others.

Affirmation: I can enjoy all that I am. I express myself freely through my body.

Bodywork therapy

"The mind's first step to self-awareness must be through the body." George Sheehan

Everything we experience is processed by both the mind and the body.

Just as our mind is part of our body, our body is part of our mind. If we need to work on our mind, we can't ignore the body.

Bodywork therapists believe that memories, traumatic or difficult emotional experiences are sometimes "somatised", held or locked inside our bodies. As a result, parts of us become stiff, frozen, floppy and sore – and numb, even – and we experience pain in these areas, or feel sluggish and lack energy and vitality.

When we hold emotional tension in our bodies, it can block the flow of our life force energy.

These somatised areas can't benefit from our natural ability to heal and repair our physical and emotional state.

Bodywork as a form of mind and body therapy originated from the work of Wilhelm Reich (who discovered 'orgone' or life force energy), Frederick Alexander (who developed the Alexander Technique), and Ida Rolf (who developed the Rolfing Technique).

If we're experiencing stressful or emotional times, regular exercise, and a massage or a stretch can help release emotional tension. Drinking plenty of water also helps calm and detoxify the body (unless you're on a long bus journey without stops!).

"Movement is a medicine for creating change in a person's physical, emotional, and mental states." Carol Welch

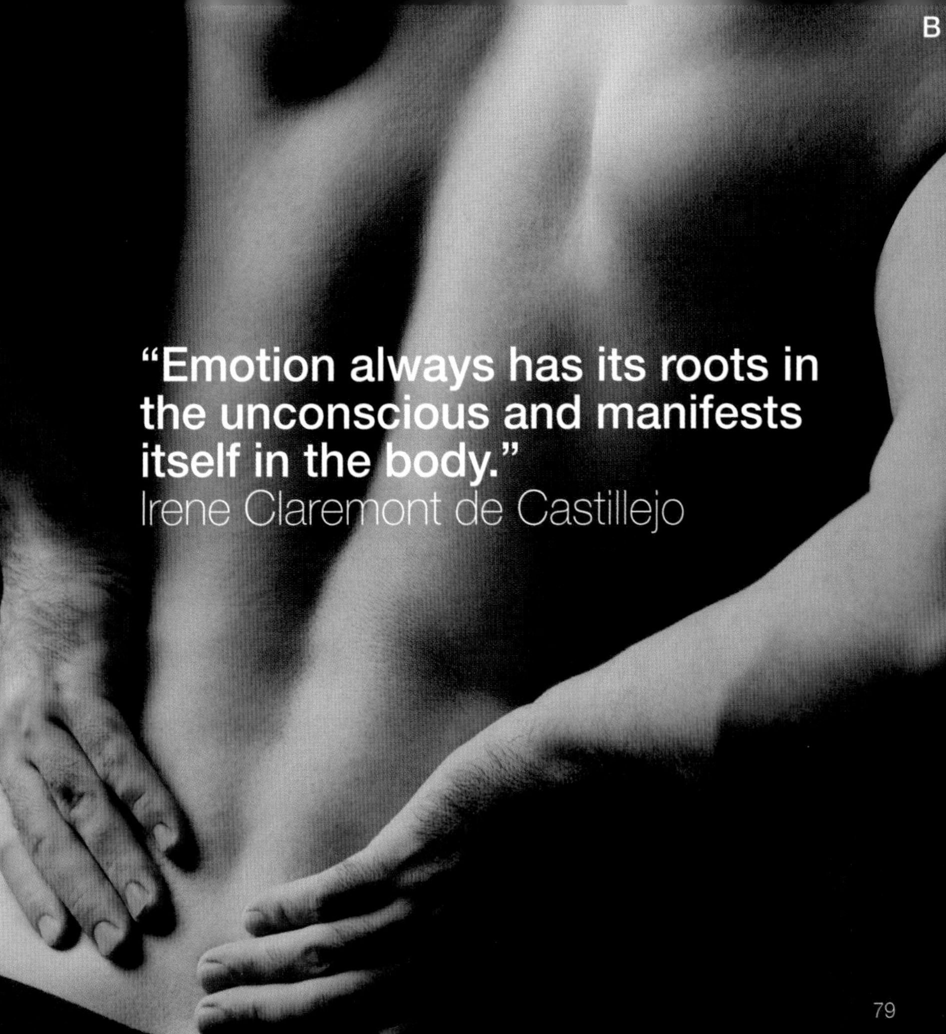

“Emotion always has its roots in the unconscious and manifests itself in the body.”
Irene Claremont de Castillejo

Boundaries

"With every new day you heal and with every new boundary you heal." Darren Bottrill

Boundaries are good for the mind.

They set psychological and emotional limits between ourselves and others. Just like having a fence around our property, we need to have fences around ourselves.

Boundaries protect us, and we need to protect our boundaries. They support us in taking care of ourselves, and they determine how far we go with people, how close we let them come or how available we make ourselves to others or situations.

Our boundaries set out what is or what isn't okay for us in our work, life and relationships. They set the limits in how we share ourselves with others. Boundaries are about distance or closeness, self-respect and value.

Boundaries can enable us to heal our minds and hearts if needs be. We can set new boundaries between ourselves and others. They can help us put a stop to old patterns or old ways of behaving or interacting with people.

Boundaries are not set out of fear or hatred but out of self-love and love for others. If we set our boundaries kindly and firmly they'll normally be appreciated in just the same way.

Reviewing and setting boundaries helps to focus and protect our mind. They can become a framework by which we take care of ourselves, and they can set limits as to how much we give of ourselves to situations or others.

Boundaries are like goal-posts or guidelines. We can move our boundaries but we need to be clear in ourselves; the clearer we are about our boundaries in our own minds, the clearer they'll be to others. (We all know how annoying it is when people keep moving the goal posts).

"A boundary is where you
end and I begin." Louise Hay

The brain

To understand the mind, it helps to understand the brain – the home of the mind after all.

The brain is 75% water. Though its mass is just 2% of the body, it uses 20% of our oxygen supply.

The brain is the central computer of our body. It controls most of our physical processes as well as intelligence and reason – the ways in which we do things, and why we do them.

The brain is responsible for our thoughts and perceptions; what we see, feel and sense. It provides us with our attention and concentration, it stores our past and it helps us process and understand the present.

The brain is in charge of how the body moves and regulates itself: body temperature, blood pressure, chemical and hormonal release.

The brain controls how we learn, how we take in information and store and recall it.

The brain controls our nervous system, the part of us that experiences life and enables us to feel and respond. Touch, taste, sight, smell and our sense of safety are all part of our nervous processes. Most of the time, we're unaware of our nervous system working (well at least until things go pear-shaped that is!).

The brain makes sense of what we experience because it's connected to the top of our spinal cord, which connects to the rest of the body through a large network of nerves, a bit like electrical cables.

These cables carry and transmit electrical messages (signals and information) from the body to the brain and from the brain back to the body.

Nerve information travels through the body at 268 miles per hour.

The signals and messages in our heads are carried by neurons, the smallest and most fundamental components of the nervous system, our electrical grid (well at least our own electricity is free – especially helpful, given the price of it today).

The brain generates enough power to run a 25 watt light bulb (how enlightening!).

Most of the "electricity" or messages carried through our body take place automatically. As well as keeping our body working, neurons give the brain important messages about what's going on around us – are we safe? Hot or cold? Is something familiar, or not?

Everything we experience in day-to-day life is processed by the nervous system and organised by our brain.

There are 15 times more neurons in a brain than there are people on the planet! That's about 100 billion neurons, more than the number of trees in the Amazon rainforest.

Brain and body functions are supported by chemicals, and our chemical levels are important. The brain needs chemicals to work, as do other parts of the body.

The brain is in charge of releasing chemicals throughout our body, our flight /flight/freeze response and our hormones. We may need adrenaline for action or serotonin to encourage us to repeat a behaviour that's helpful for the survival of the human race.

The chemical levels in our body are affected by the nutrients we take in and the ways we rest and sleep. If the chemical levels in our brain become unbalanced so do we (believe me, I've been there).

If we don't get enough sunlight, our melatonin levels can drop.

If we overload on stress, our serotonin suffers. If we eat too much sugar, our insulin level changes.

If we're bored, isolated or inactive, this can affect dopamine levels.

If the chemical balance in our brain gets depleted, we may need medication to restore or replenish it.

People trained to deal specifically with brain and brain chemicals are neurologists or psychiatrists.

Doctors are able to prescribe medication for the mind too (but be mindful, it's not a cure!).

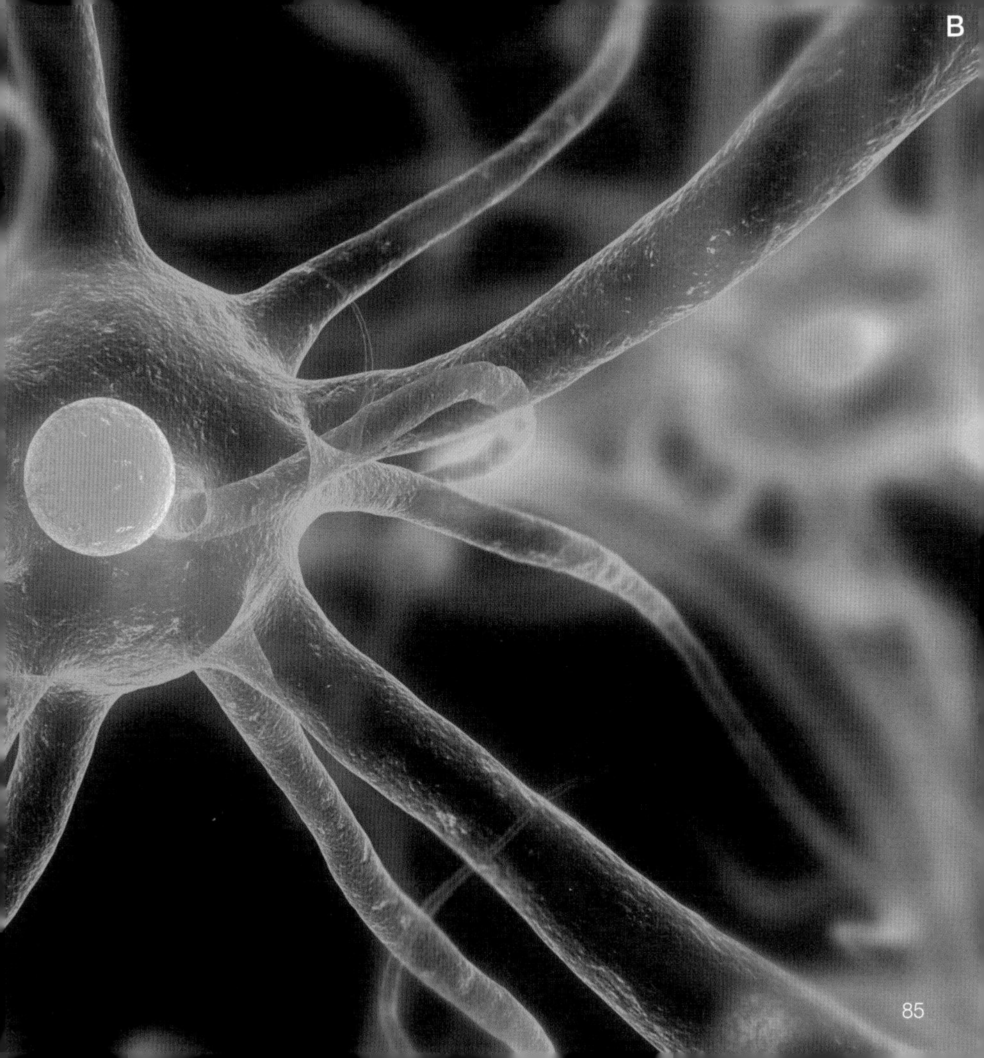
B

Breath and breathing

Without food we can live for 30 days, without water we live for six. But without oxygen we last six minutes! (and without alcohol who cares!)

The air around us is 78% nitrogen and 21% oxygen. (It's oxygen that keeps us going not caffeine!)

Breathing is something we do without realising; it's an involuntary bodily function. We don't have to remember to breathe (it's one of the things we can do in sleep).

Our respiratory system is both voluntary and involuntary; this means we can control it. We can't voluntarily stop or start our heart, but we can control how we breathe. As we become aware of our breath and learn how to use it, it's a powerful tool to manage the mind.

When we sigh, we take a breath three times larger than a normal one.

The breath is the bridge between our mind and body. How we breathe and what we breathe affects our body. In the same way, what goes on inside us affects our breath. If we feel frightened, angry or sexually excited our breath changes – it may quicken or become shallower. When we're relaxed, our breath may slow down and deepen.

Nearly all of us breathe in a shallow way. But when we breathe fully and deeply we can take fewer breaths, helping slow the heart rate, reducing anxiety and, if we do enough deep, slow breathing, increasing longevity (alcohol just pickles us!).

By the time we reach 70 we'll have taken over 600 million breaths!

By controlling our breath we can, to some extent, control our mind and body.

With deep and slow breaths we take in more air, there's more oxygen available so our heart can slow down and this can slow other systems – in particular the nervous one.

The lungs are the only organs that can float (though I'd rather not find out!).

By breathing deeply and slowly for a few minutes our parasympathetic system can kick in. This is the part of our autonomic arousal system that works when we're relaxed, comfortable, warm and satisfied.

The average person breathes in around 8000 litres of air daily. Worldwide that's 544 000 000 000 000 litres of air a day (pity we can't keep it cleaner).

By breathing more fully and slowly we feel calmer; the breath helps to centre our mind and body, especially if we're experiencing pain or stressful situations, and this helps us cope better.

By focusing our mind on our breath, our thought processes slow down, and this affects how we feel and can reduce anxiety or panic.

The surface area of the lungs is around the same size as a tennis court.

Breathing can help improve our sexual experiences (now you're interested). Taking deep breaths while we make love can help us control when we climax. Breathing deeply allows more blood to flow to our genitals, increasing their sensitivity and the pleasurable feelings and sensations we have.

Relaxation classes, meditation and yoga can teach us how to breathe more effectively (see p.222).

Bulimia nervosa

Bulimia nervosa is an eating disorder linked to self-esteem, emotional problems and stress.

Bulimia is more common than anorexia nervosa, but much easier to hide. In the UK, between 1 and 3 per cent of young women are thought to be bulimic at any given moment in time.

If we experience bulimia we tend to think about what we eat all the time. We can get caught in a cycle of eating large amounts, then making ourselves sick, then starving, or find other ways to make up for the amount we've eaten. With bulimia, we may constantly count the calories we consume or diet all of the time.

There are physical and emotional signs of bulimia. We might have a sore throat, bad breath or puffy cheeks, or feel dehydrated all the time. We might get tummy ache or constipation, or our periods become irregular. We may feel depressed or low.

We may experience mood swings or feel out of control, and we can become obsessed with dieting.

Although bulimia may not involve the weight loss experienced with anorexia nervosa, it's just as serious. Persistent vomiting is extremely harmful to our body, it can alter our electrolyte balance. Electrolytes are the salts that help our body conduct electrical impulses which enable vital bodily functions. Changes to our electrolytes can be fatal, at worst it can cause our heart to stop.

Help is available to those with bulimia and caring for someone with the illness.Our first point of call is our GP. Then there are many organisations and support groups that help people recover from bulimia. Talking to a doctor or counsellor can provide us with more information and support.

Many experts who help people with eating disorders believe the sooner we get help, the sooner we can start to treat and overcome our condition.

B
According to B-eat, today between 1 and 3% of young women in the UK are thought to be bulimic at any given moment in time.

Caffeine

One of the primary causes of high anxiety is caffeine. Caffeine is a psychotropic drug found in coffee, chocolate, tea, soft drinks and a fair few prescription drugs (as well as ProPlus tablets!).

For most of us, caffeine in small doses is harmless, but some of us are more sensitive to it than others. Too much can trigger recognisable signs of mental illness. The American Psychiatric Association classifies Caffeine Intoxification as a mental disorder!

John F Greden, the former Director of Psychiatric Research at the Walter Reed Army Medical Centre, Washington DC, has pointed out that symptoms of caffeinism are "essentially indistinguishable from those of anxiety neurosis".

Caffeine is also used in headache tablets, as it increases the rate at which the body absorbs pain relieving and other chemicals.

Caffeine can affect our hormone levels. It slows the absorption of the hormone adenosine, which calms us. Caffeine also helps release adrenaline into our body, which helps us wake up – but then, as the adrenaline drops again, we feel tired and low.

Caffeine can also increase the level of cortisol in our body. This is a stress-sensitive hormone that regulates our mood, weight and blood sugar level. If too much cortisol is released at once, it will affect how we feel, and over a period of time it can change our weight.

Caffeine also affects our dopamine levels, Dopamine is released from the caffeine hit and for a while we feel good, but the feeling soon subsides.

Caffeine is a stimulant: if we're prone to anxiety, panic or depression it's worth watching how much we consume.

C
Caffeine was first separated from coffee in the 1800s. Today, it's the world's most popular drug.

C
When we cry our body releases a stress-sensitive chemical called prolactin. Crying enables our body to release any build up of this hormone which physically reduces our stress.

Catharsis

Catharsis is a Greek word meaning to “purge” or “cleanse”.

Catharsis is important for a happy, healthy mind. When we laugh, cry or share our feelings, this releases their psychic energy, helping clear and calm our mind.

But when we bottle up stress or sadness, this can block our energy pathways and capacity to heal. So at times we need to get in touch with our feelings and let them out in the way that that’s right for us (as long as we don’t “dump” them onto other people!).

Catharsis helps clear our heads. When we laugh we feel good, and after we’ve been crying we feel calmer.

Some of us hold onto hurts, but it’s hard to heal them if we don’t let them out.

We’re not always encouraged to cry when we’re sad, which is a pity, because releasing sadness in this way helps restore our mind and well-being.

Tears contain prolactin, a stress hormone, so when we cry our body is physically getting rid of the stress.

Holding onto emotion requires a great deal of physical and psychological energy. So as we release old feelings we make space for happiness.

Sharing our thoughts, worries or woes is also cathartic. At times, we just need to share where we’re at (for crying out loud!). We all need to be heard and we all need to feel.

Many counsellors and psychotherapists believe that catharsis is an important part of the healing and recovery process.

Change

"The key to change is to let go of fear." Roseanne Cash

If we want to heal our heads or our hearts, we need to start by changing our minds. Most of us are capable of change – it might seem scary, but in order to grow, move on or recover we may need to change how we think or what we do.

We may want a new job, new direction or relationship. We may have to change to keep these things. How we manage and bring about change is down to our state of mind.

"Change your thoughts and you change your world."
Norman Vincent Peale

Change involves courage. We may have to change jobs to reduce stress, or leave a relationship that makes us unhappy. We may have to change habits to recover from addiction, or change how we think to heal our depression.

"It's not that some people have willpower and some don't. It's that some people are ready to change and others are not."
James Gordon MD

Change, like loss, can be difficult and painful. We may need support, medication or time, but change opens doors to new opportunities. As we decide to change, we can gain new insights and resources within. But they can't be discovered if we don't want to change.

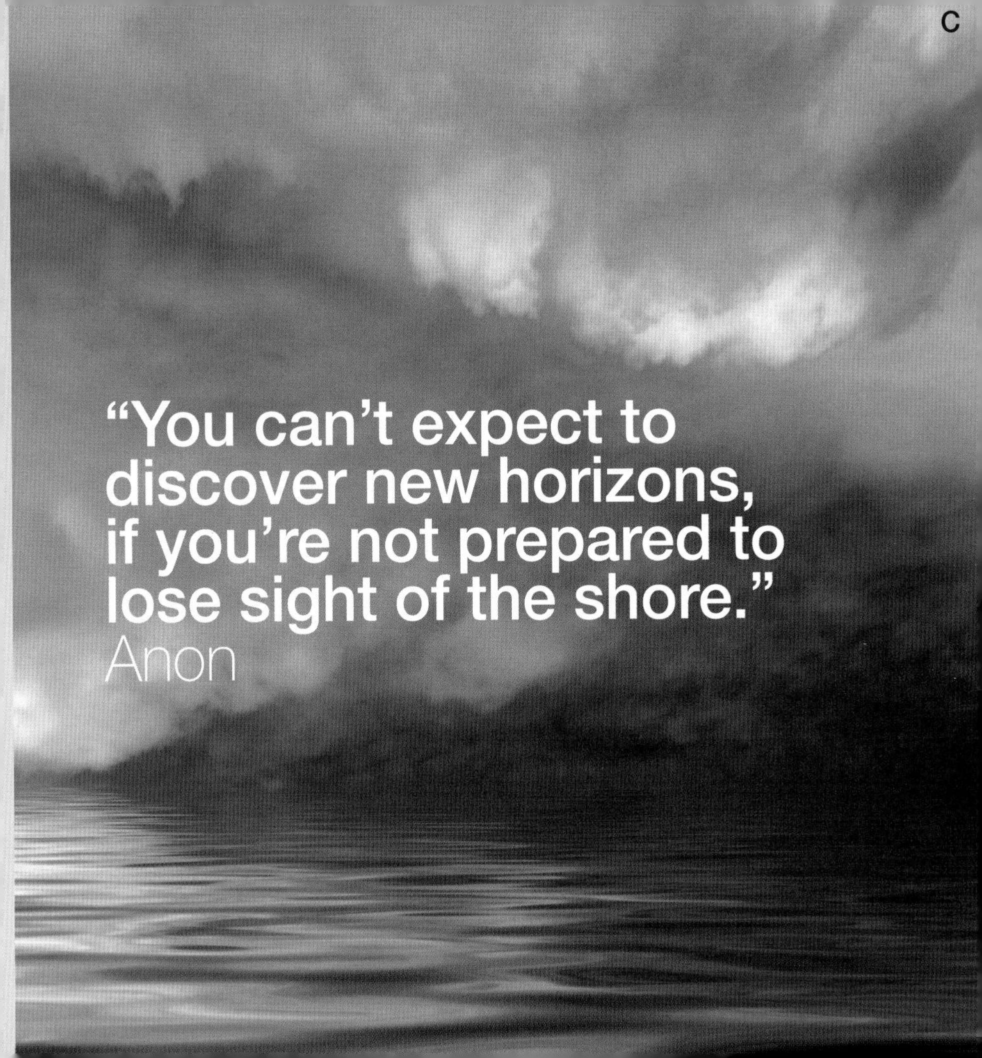

C

“You can’t expect to discover new horizons, if you’re not prepared to lose sight of the shore.”

Anon

Child psychology

(The science of getting your child to eat food by pretending it is mud!)

Child psychologists are specially trained in the mental, emotional and social development of children. A child psychologist is a clinical psychologist trained specifically to work with the general needs of kids. An educational psychologist is trained to help young people in the learning environment.

What do you call a child who's good but breaks things? Smashing!!!

Clinical psychologists

"Clinical psychologists aim to reduce psychological distress and to enhance and promote psychological well-being. They deal with mental and physical health problems including anxiety, depression, relationship problems, addictions and relationships.Clinical psychologists deal with both adults and children, so if you are looking for a "child psychologist" you may well want someone with a clinical background."
British Psychological Society.

Clinical psychologists work in health and social care settings, including hospitals, health centres, community mental health teams, child and adolescent mental health services, and social services. They tend to work with social workers, doctors and other health professionals. Most work for the NHS but some work privately. They to assess and explore people's needs and to provide therapies and treatment based on psychological theory and research.

Codependency

The term codependent is often attached to alcoholism or addiction but all of us have the capacity to be codependent, especially if we look at our relationships!

Codependency was put on the map by Melody Beattie, author of *Codependent No More* and *Beyond Codependency*.

When we're codependent we depend upon others to feel okay – both in ourselves and in our world. We tend to put others' needs before our own, and accommodate others to such an extent that we negate or ignore our own feelings, needs and wants. How we feel about ourselves depends upon how successful we are at pleasing or taking care of others.

If we experience codependency, our life and relationships can be difficult and painful. If we rely on others to meet our personal needs we're constantly in their power. We look to others to make us feel whole rather than feeling complete and fulfilled as we are, in ourselves.

Codependent relationships undermine our ability to be independent and to relate comfortably to other people outside the relationship; instead we fulfil ourselves through the life and love of another. A codependent relationship can be unreliable, emotionally unstable and far from secure. One partner may be needy, and the other may control in response to that need.

The talking therapies can help us understand our codependency issues. We may need to work through old patterns or hurts; in time, we can learn how to love ourselves and meet our needs from within.

Some marriages are an example of codependency.

For some, marriage is a three-ring circus: engagement ring, wedding ring, suffering!

Affirmation: I can learn how to love myself and put myself first.

"No one should part with their individuality and become that of another." William Ellery Channing

Cognitive Behavioural Therapy (CBT)

CBT is a talking therapy that encourages us to explore how we think about ourselves, others and the world around us. CBT helps us understand how what we do affects our thoughts and feelings.

CBT examines how we think (cognitions) and how we act (behaviour). Changing how we think enables us to feel better and do better. CBT works with the here and now, and it's focused on exploring our present experience rather than the past.

CBT can be helpful if we experience anxiety, depression, panic attacks, phobias, bulimia, obsessive-compulsive disorder and schizophrenia.

CBT helps us break down problems into smaller parts. We can separate challenges into situations or events, then separate out the thoughts, emotions, physical feelings and actions that follow. The different parts of any given situation can affect each other, and how we think about them will affect how we feel or what we do.

As we break down our experiences into manageable pieces, we're able to find new ways of dealing with each of them, and then we can begin to explore new approaches in thinking and doing.

"Men are disturbed not by things, but by the view which they take of them." Epictetus (but, what about women?)

The concepts that influenced the development of CBT have been around for thousands of years, but CBT as a therapy emerged during the 1960s.

American psychotherapist Albert Ellis believed that most of our problems are caused by irrational thought distortions – “shoulds” or “musts” – “I should do well”, ”you must treat me well”, “the world ‘must’ / ‘should’ be easy” (if only!).

Ellis developed Rational Emotive Behavioural Therapy (REBT), which influenced the work of Aaron Beck who developed Cognitive Therapy, which has become CBT today.

Beck believed the mind has schemas, and that these schemas organise our experiences and behaviour, our beliefs and rules. Our schemas influence our reality, how we experience events – a bit like spectacles, they alter how we see things.

Schemas provide the framework upon which we hang our reality. If we begin to explore and challenge our schemas, we can learn to see things differently and behave differently.

The idea of our sense of “reality” being determined by our thoughts is not a new one.

The philosopher Immanuel Kant (1724–1804) believed that reality is never directly knowable, but that it’s “known” through “categories” of thinking!

Communication

A man calls his doctor: "My wife' s pregnant, her contractions are only two minutes apart!"

"Is this her first child?" the doctor enquires…

"No, you idiot, this is her husband!"

Communication is about how we hear and see things as well as what we say and do!

Communication is important to all of us. It's the way we relate to others and how we clarify or check things out. Communication enables us to express our responses and feelings, and it's the tool we use to share thoughts, ideas and our needs and wants (it's not just about having a mobile phone).

We learn about communication from our early experiences. We're taught what we "should" or "shouldn't" say – what's okay to share and also what isn't.

Most of the time what we've learned is helpful, but we can all improve the way we use words.

We may need to learn how to share feelings, or how to be assertive and get ourselves heard. Some of us take criticism far better than a compliment, and most of us listen but decide what we hear.

We all use words in different ways. How we relate to others reflects how we relate within. How we talk to ourselves is just as important as the way we talk to others. Are our words caring, supportive and positive? Or critical, harsh and unkind?

"When you don't know what you're talking about, it's hard to know when you're finished." Tommy Smothers

Our mind is an essential part of our communication system. It can help us choose what to say, and when (or not, as the case may be).

Our mind develops through our interactions with others – the things we learned or were told as kids, and the things we hear now which stimulate thought.

When we were small, our minds were like tape decks, and the recordings we made then still influence how we think.

If the communication around us was healthy and positive, it's likely we'll think in the same way now. But if the messages were hurtful, negative or shaming they get recorded and played out just the same.

What we recorded while young is known as our "self talk" – the messages in our mind that affect how we think, feel and act. If our self-talk is positive we're more able to cope with life, but negative self-talk can make us feel low.

The messages we hold in the back of our mind can make a huge difference to how we experience life today.

If the words in our heads are happy and positive, they will influence how we experience life, but if the messages are old, unhelpful and negative … it might be time to re-write the tapes. A counsellor or therapist can help us with this.

"The word 'politics' is derived from the word 'poly', meaning 'many', and the word 'ticks', meaning 'blood sucking parasites'."
Larry Hardiman

The more effective our communication, the more we're able to get our needs met. Communication leads to recognition, the no. 1 human need and recognition can help us with confidence (see p.298).

Affirmation: I express myself freely. I can experiment with ways of getting understood.

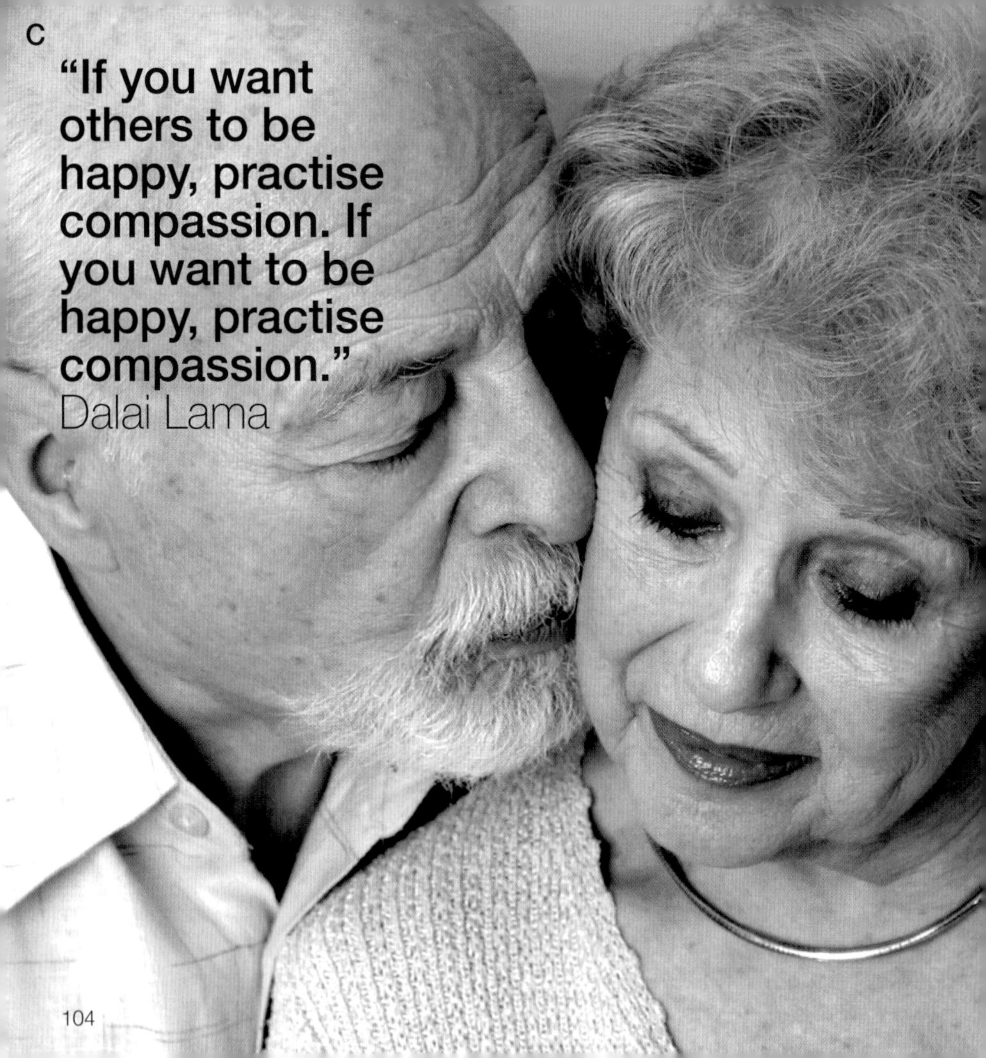

C

"If you want others to be happy, practise compassion. If you want to be happy, practise compassion."
Dalai Lama

Compassion

We all need a bit of compassion (and passion) at times – it's the milk of human kindness that heals and helps us through.

"Compassion is not religious business, it is human business, it is not luxury, it is essential for our own peace and mental stability, it is essential for human survival."
Dalai Lama

The word compassion comes from Latin – "com"- meaning "with", and "passio", suffering.

Compassion allows us to experience our own suffering and to share in the pain of others.

We've all taken the hits from life; compassion arrives as we accept and heal. It helps us acknowledge what's gone before us and deal with what's left as we leave it behind.

Compassion is about love and understanding, feeling our feelings and owning our pain. As we feel for ourselves we can feel for others; as we understand ourselves, we can understand others.

Compassion allows us to be emotionally involved without being overwhelmed. Meanwhile, compassion from others gives us support and strength. Compassion within is soothing and sensitive. As we become kinder to ourselves, we become kinder to others.

Affirmation: I give myself and others unconditional love.

C
Confidence is a bit like a bucket with a hole in: we have to keep topping it up!

Confidence

When we're confident we have faith in ourselves. We're able to take risks, explore new avenues and deal with unknown outcomes (like kids!).

Some of us are more confident than others. Confidence is learned and nurtured; we can learn to be confident just as easily as we unlearn it. Confidence is gained through how we think and act; it is our thoughts and actions that make us feel confident.

"Inaction breeds doubt and fear. Action breeds confidence and courage, if you want to conquer fear, don't sit and think about it. Go out and get busy!" Dale Carnegie

Confidence comes from our self-esteem, how we value ourselves and what we believe about ourselves. Some of us learned confidence from our parents and caregivers – we were praised, valued, encouraged and supported. If this wasn't the case we may feel low in self-confidence – but it's something we can strengthen.

We can let life and people shake our confidence. It's a bit like a bucket with a hole in – we need to keep it topped up. If we think confident and talk confident, although at first it may seem uncomfortable and even "fake", when we get over that, we'll soon feel and act the same way naturally.

Improving self-confidence takes belief, courage and action. Talking to someone compassionate and responsive when our confidence is low can give us a boost and build us back up.

"You gain strength, courage, and confidence by every experience in which you really stop to look fear in the face. You must do the thing which you think you cannot do." Eleanor Roosevelt

Consciousness

Sigmund Freud developed The Model of Mind. He defined consciousness as a part of our 'psyche' (mind), along with the pre-conscious and unconscious parts of it.

For Freud, consciousness was the part of our mind that's in touch with reality as we each individually define it. Consciousness is the doorway between the world we experience and the world within – i.e. the unconscious and preconscious parts of our mind.

Consciousness is the part we know as "I", "me", "myself".

Our sense of consciousness is like our state of awareness: we're conscious of some things and unconscious of others. We can be self-conscious too – aware that others are aware of us!

Our state of consciousness can develop and grow; if we are conscious of what we do and how we think or feel, we're able to observe this – and, if need be, change it.

Psychotherapy can help us develop our consciousness and self-awareness. As we explore our conscious mind, we can begin to understand what we do and why we do it. In time, we can use our mind more effectively.

Consciousness:
That annoying time between naps (and beer sessions).

Counselling

"Counselling takes place when a counsellor sees a client in a private and confidential setting to explore a difficulty the client is having, a distress they may be experiencing or perhaps a dissatisfaction with life, or loss of a sense of direction or purpose. It is always at the request of the client, no one can be sent for counselling" British Association for Counselling and Psychotherapy (BACP.)

"84% of adults in the UK have or would consider going for counselling or psychotherapy." BACP

Counselling can help us develop our self-awareness. Talking to a counsellor can help us gain insight and find new strengths and ways of doing things that can improve the way we cope with our lives.

"72% of people have said they would feel happier if they talked about their problems with a counsellor or psychotherapist." BACP

Counselling helps us explore and understand our challenges, it helps us discover new ways of dealing with life or coming to terms with it!

Counselling involves listening, facilitation and support; it is not about persuasion or getting advice.

"Nearly 1 in 2 employees in Great Britain have expressed a desire to go to confidential counselling should the employer provide it." BACP

There are different types of counsellors. Some are trained in specific areas such as bereavement, alcoholism, domestic abuse and couples counselling.

There's a list of organisations that list qualified counsellors at the back of this book.

C
According to the British Association for Counselling and Psychotherapy (BACP) “nearly 1 in 2 employees in Great Britain have expressed a desire to go to confidential counselling should the employer provide it.”

Crying

French proverb say "life is an onion, one peels it crying" (or when someone kicks sand in your eyes).

Crying releases and communicates emotion. It's good for the heart and for our heads. All of us cried before we could talk. Babies cry in distress or discomfort, but don't produce tears until they are 6–8 weeks old.

Crying, also known as lacrimation, is a way of releasing and expressing emotion. It also releases toxins from the body; the tears we produce are made up of water, mucus and chemical toxins.

When we cry we release prolactin, a stress sensitive hormone that builds up in response to stress, so that as we cry we feel calmer. Releasing prolactin reduces the level of anxiety and tension in our body.

When we cry our nose might run (well not literally), tears sometimes drain through our nostrils (well, better that way than the other way round!).

Teardrops are surrounded by a layer of oil which holds the liquid inside. The oil stops the tear falling out of our eye before it has cleansed or cleared it.

Basal tears wash our eyes as we blink, and we blink 10 million times a year. Reflex tears flow in response to irritants like onions or smoke (or people even!). Emotional tears respond to a feeling, which could be pride, happiness or sadness.

Holding back tears does more harm than good. Researchers and therapists believe that weeping and sobbing is important to healing.

Affirmation: It's okay to cry and enjoy the satisfying feeling of releasing my emotions.

C
Our eyes blink up to
10 million times a year!

Dementia

Dementia describes a group of diseases that affect our brain function. Some 60 illnesses, including Alzheimer's, Huntington's and Parkinson's, can cause dementia.

Though dementia is mostly linked to age, little is known as to the specific causes but the symptoms are all too familiar.

Dementia is a gradual illness where we slowly lose our ability to function. We lose our memory and experience confusion; it can also affect our personality and behaviour.

Dementia is a condition for which there's not yet a cure. Medication can't reverse its effects. It's a degenerative illness that just takes its course, deeply frustrating for both sufferer and carers.

If we experience dementia, our mind gradually stops working the way it used to, which makes it harder to manage day-to-day things. We become less able to fend for ourselves, to think, remember or cope with our life.

Though mostly associated with old age, only 1 in 5 people over 80 develop it.

The Alzheimer's Society estimate over 700 000 people in the UK have the condition and that 20 000 of them are under 65.

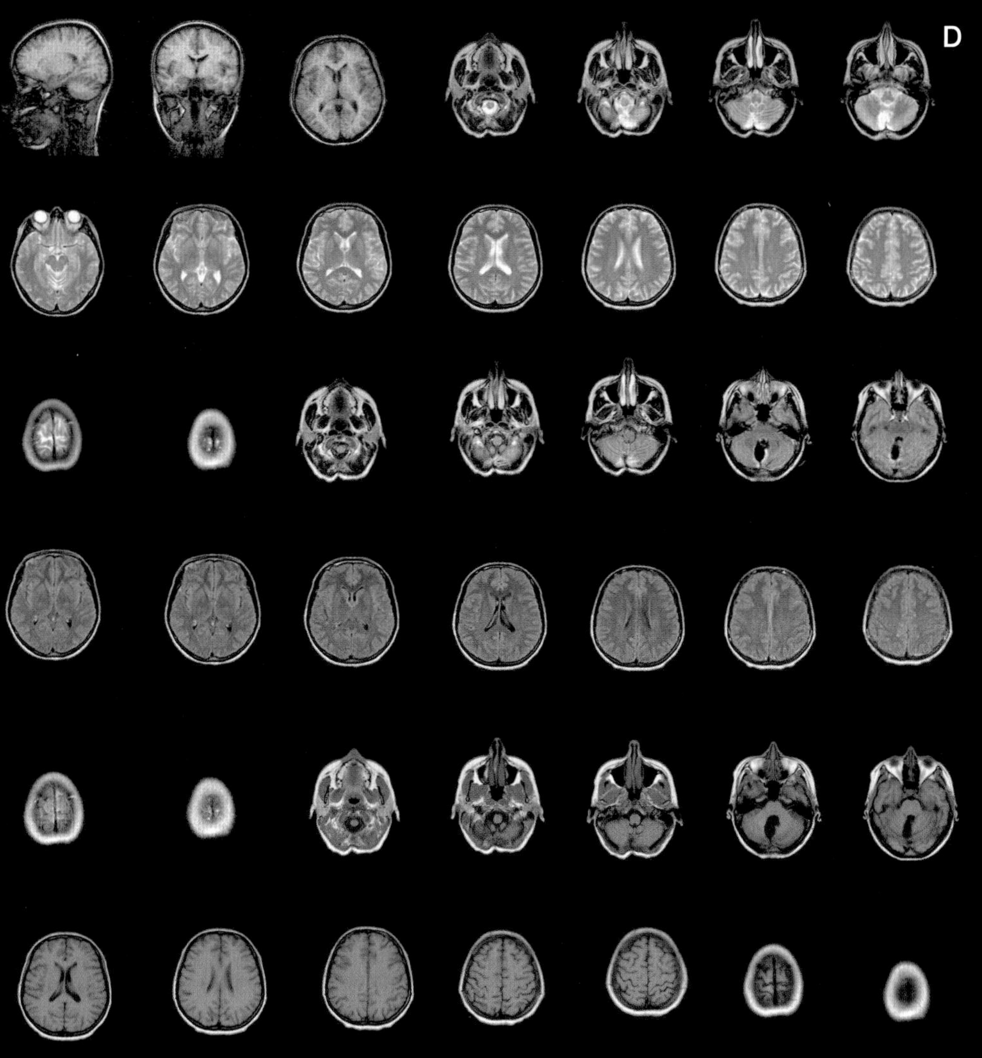
D

Depression

According to the World Health Organization, some 121 million people experience diagnosed depression world wide – that's 2% of the entire population!

In the UK, 8 -12% of the population experience depression in any given year.

50% of people who visit the doctors are experiencing some form of depression (wonder what the other 50% have got?).

According to the World Health Organization, depression is the leading cause of disability across the world.

Depression is the most common dis-ease of the mind.

We've all experienced some level of depression; it reveals itself in a number of ways and is more than being sad.

Depression is a defence against anxiety. We experience depression as our body shuts down in response to an overload of adrenaline.

Exercise can help depression (and anxiety). It helps our body discharge adrenalin through movement.

If we experience depression, we have long periods of low mood, unable to feel good or a sense of pleasure. It affects our self-esteem and self-confidence, and can lead to a feeling of hopelessness and despair.

Depression can cause us to lose our appetite and sex drive or affect our ability to sleep. It can be hard for us to concentrate, socialise or work. We may feel lethargic or unable to cope. At worst, we may attempt suicide.

"Depression is not sobbing and crying and giving vent, it is plain and simple reduction of feeling ... People who keep stiff upper lips find that it's damn hard to smile."
Judith Guest

Many things can lead to depression; we can develop the condition from a loss or trauma we're finding hard to accept, if we've bottled up sadness or anger inside, we may find releasing it eases our mind.

Depression can be caused by the way we think. If our thoughts are negative they can make us feel down. We can learn to think better, which can indeed lift our mood.

There are different types of depression: clinical depression, postnatal depression, seasonal affective disorder, manic depression (or bipolar as it is now called) and cyclothymic disorder (which describes mood swings).

Depression can affect all areas of our life, how we work, how we love, how we feel, think and do. We can become withdrawn or feel isolated, as if no one wants to be with us when we're blue.

Depression is a treatable condition, especially if we can discover what's causing it – and therein lies our cure.

Antidepressants can restore our brain chemicals, which helps lift our mood and relieve the symptoms of depression but they don't cure it (see p.36).

It can be hard to relate to why someone's depressed, but with time and talking, belief and commitment, it's possible to heal the condition long term.

Determination

"The difference between the possible and the impossible lies in a person's determination." Tommy Lasorda

Determination focuses our mind and gives us the drive and belief to succeed.

From overcoming anxiety to ending an addiction, from ending a relationship to starting a business, from recovering from burnout to building a home, from losing a loved one to finding new friends – anything's possible if we're determined enough.

"Success means having the courage, the determination, and the will to become the person you believe you were meant to be." George Sheehan

Determination is not something we have – it's something we learn and give to ourselves. Determination directs the mind, channels our thoughts, beliefs and energy and gives us the will to keep going.

"If you think you can do a thing or think you can't do a thing, you're right." Henry Ford

Determination delivers our dreams…

We all have dreams; our mind creates them and can help us fulfill them (if we believe in them enough!).

"Follow your dream! Unless it's the one where you're at work in your underwear during a fire drill"

Anon

Whether it's raising a family, getting a new job or buying that house in the country, we all need dreams. They get us going, and when we're going we're on our way.

"You are never too old to set another goal or to dream a new dream." C.S. Lewis

If we believe in our dreams they become goals, and our goals give us something to head for in life.

If we're facing tough times, we need to take time to dream. If we believe in our dreams they light sparks within and give us new goals to get back on track.

Dreams, like goals, set destinations, point us to a direction in life we're choosing to take.

When we know we've got choices we can use them to get what we want out of life.

Affirmation: I trust I can get to where I want to be.

"Don't be pushed by your problems. Be led by your dreams."
Anon

D

Discounts

The term “discount” can be used to describe a form of behaviour and communication that belongs to the world of Transactional Analysis (see p.340).

Discounts deny, ignore or avoid reality – in ourselves, in others or in a given situation.

We discount ourselves when we say “we can’t” or fail to see our ability to do something. We may discount our feelings and deny their importance, and we can discount the strengths that we have to get through.

We discount others by disregarding their feelings or the reality they share or make known. We discount others if we protect their feelings or don’t tell them we’re angry in case they get upset. We discount their ability to cope with our truth.

We discount situations when we fail to see danger or all the complexities that have led to events. When we do that, we can’t prepare for or see opportunities that could come about.

We all use discounts from time to time but they get in the way of getting on. If we constantly deny our capability or options, it limits the way we approach life.

Discounts support old ways of thinking, and patterns and beliefs we think we can’t change. As we explore and develop our thinking, however, we can increase our sense of self-worth, which reduces our need to use discounts. (We should put our price up, not down!)

Affirmation: I communicate openly, I ask for what I want and need clearly and directly.

Dissociative disorders

The mind not only wanders, sometimes it leaves completely!

Our sense of identity and reality is derived from our memory, thoughts and perceptions. If these parts of our mind disconnect from each other, it can change who we are and how we see our world.

Dissociation happens when the parts of our mind that inform our reality become detached or disconnected from each other.

We've all experienced dissociation at some point; it's a defence mechanism that helps us cope with trauma. It also kicks in when we've too much on our mind (how many times have you got into the car, driven a familiar route and not remembered a moment of it?).

Dissociation becomes a disorder if we experience it repeatedly or most of the time. There are different types of dissociative disorders, from amnesia and post-traumatic stress disorder to multiple personality disorder, each very treatable in its own way.

Medication can help symptoms of dissociation, which include anxiety, depression or insomnia, and many people believe the best recovery route is talking to others or a counsellor or therapist.

By sharing what may have caused our dissociation, we can gradually connect with all of our parts. By slowly and safely exploring our experiences, we may no longer need to disconnect from ourselves and can come to terms with the trauma we've faced.

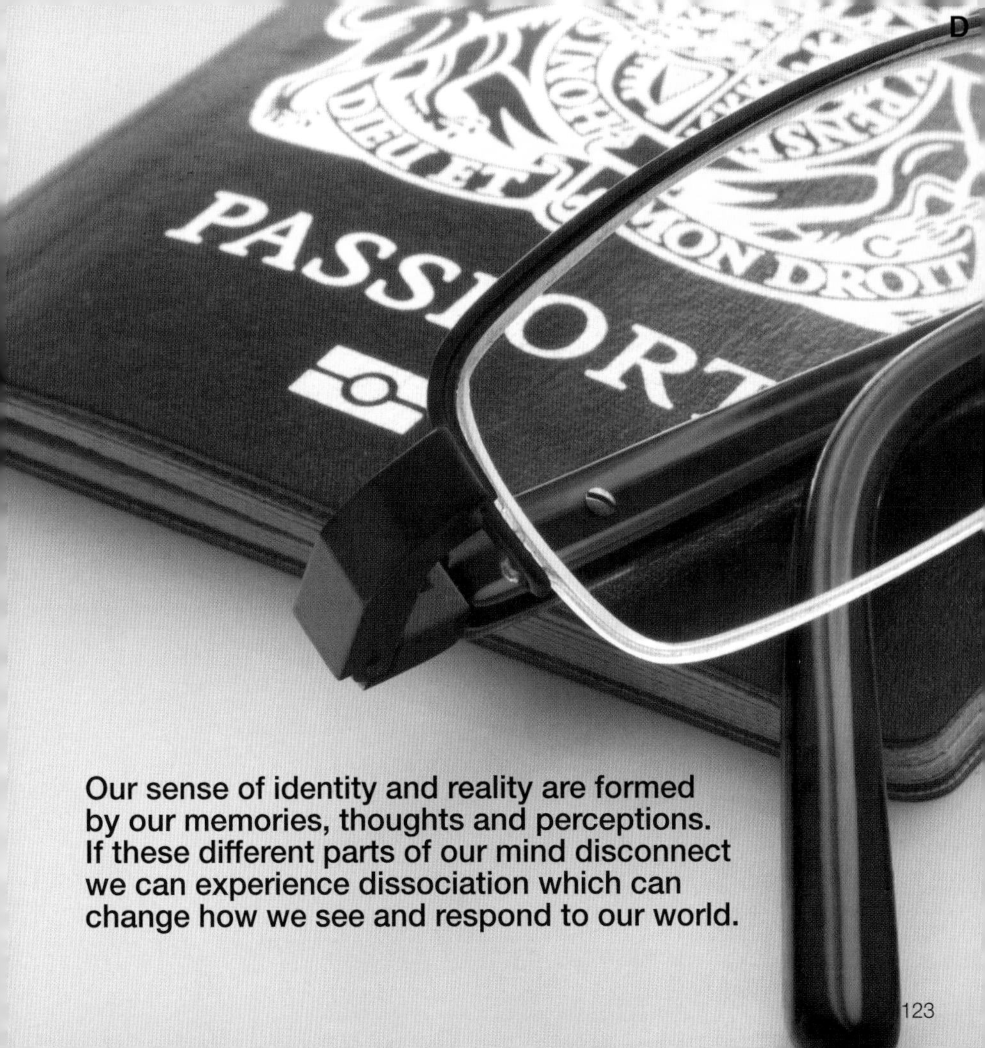

Our sense of identity and reality are formed by our memories, thoughts and perceptions. If these different parts of our mind disconnect we can experience dissociation which can change how we see and respond to our world.

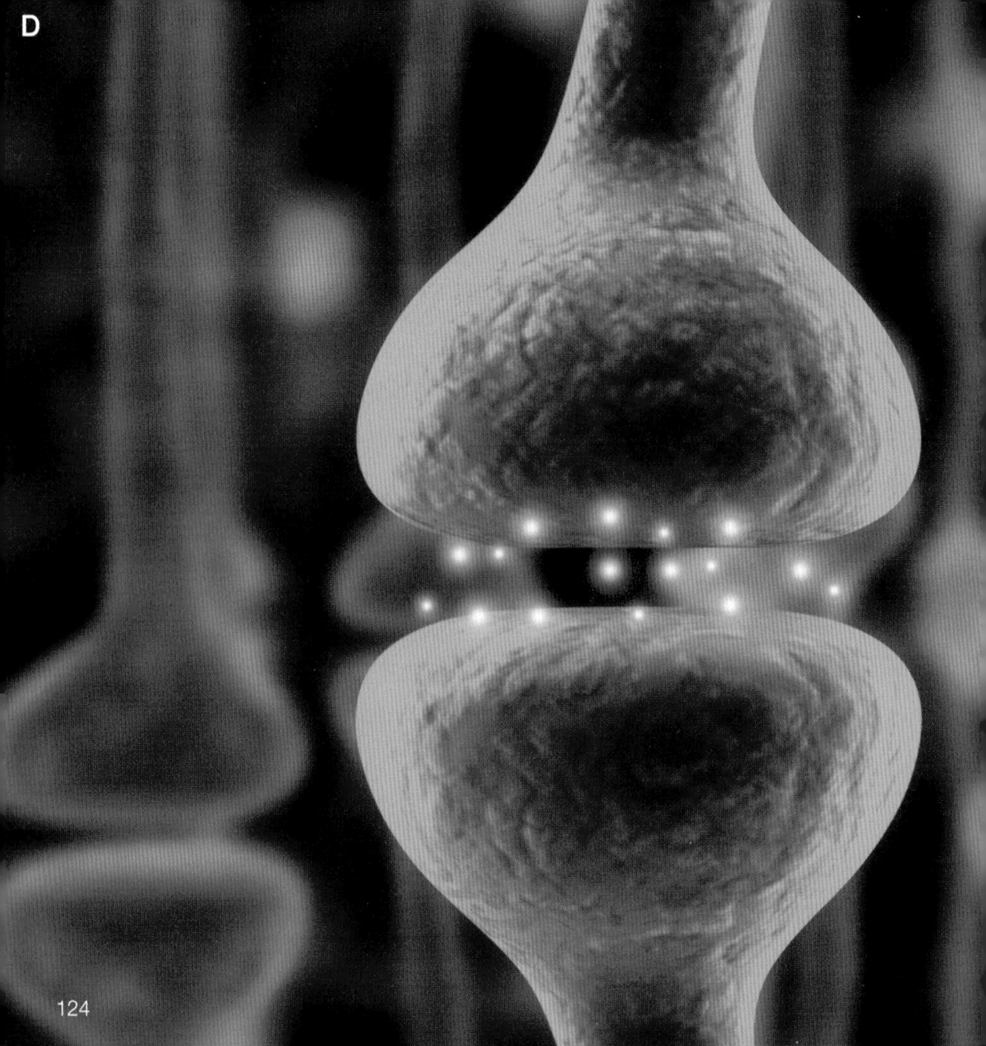
D

Dopamine

Dopamine is the chemical that makes us feel great. (It provides the biggest legal blast that we can get, just before we orgasm – it builds up before climax and drops when we're done).

Dopamine is a neurotransmitter, a brain chemical that helps movement, sleep and our attention to things, our sensory perception and our sense of reality. It's a chemical we release as we experience pleasure – enjoying nice food or sexual intimacy.

Our dopamine levels determine our behaviour. It drives our need for reward and good feelings. Its level can increase as we take risks or achieve the goals we want from our life. Cocaine and heroin affect dopamine too; it's the brain chemical most associated with craving.

When our level of dopamine is too high we can become hyper-vigilant, wired, paranoid or suspicious. If the level is too low we may find it difficult to concentrate or attend to tasks.

Dopamine is the chemical that can cause psychosis, where we lose touch with our sense of reality. Antipsychotic drugs change our dopamine levels, enabling us to see things more clearly (see p.40).

Dopamine is made by the brain. Foods such as apples, chicken, cottage cheese, fish and wheat germ contain a chemical called phenylalanine, which helps our head make dopamine (so if we're not having orgasms, we should have good food!).

The Drama Triangle

The TA (Transactional Analysis) therapist Stephen B Karpman developed the Drama Triangle in 1968. It's a way of exploring how we all interact and the role of power in the way we relate.

There are three positions in the Drama Triangle; each explores one of the kinds of role we assume as we meet others or life events – are we a Victim, Persecutor or Rescuer?

The victim is a bit of a "poor me"; we may feel disempowered because we're being persecuted or feel we need a knight in shining armour to rescue us.

The persecutor takes a stance of blame – nothing is ever, ever their fault, and they like to be 'one up' all the time – the way they do this is by picking a victim (nice).

The rescuer gallops in, putting all their effort into the needs of others whilst negating the needs of their own.

Every rescuer needs a victim – it helps them feel better about who they are.

We've all played a part on the drama triangle. It's part of life and attracts hidden agendas. The role of victim, persecutor or rescuer can be something we adopt in a particular event or become a theme throughout life.

The more we strengthen our individual identity and hold our own in life, the less we need to take part in a triangle. As we develop our sense of self and become aware of our capabilities, we won't need others to rescue or blame us. We can be our own knight and gallop away. If we're determined we can – we will.

Affirmation: I can hold my own in my life and relationships.

D

Dreaming

The average human being dreams around 2 hours a night, so we spend 6 years of our life dreaming (that's just when we're asleep!).

Little is known about the content of dreaming, but we know that dreams, like sleep, ease the mind.

As we dream we experience images, thoughts and feelings. Dreams can give us clues as to where we're at (particularly the one where we can't run away or appear naked in public!) but there's no empirical understanding of the world where we dream.

Research shows that the brain is more active when we're asleep than when we're awake.

Our dreaming sleep is linked to REM, rapid eye movement. Evidence suggests we experience dreams while we're in REM – this type of sleep is the most restorative for the brain.

During REM, the brain stops chemical reactions such as the release of serotonin and noradrenaline. This causes REM atonia, a temporary and voluntary state of paralysis. The motor neurons that make us move stop working when we're in REM (and I don't mean the band!).

Eugene Aserinkskey discovered REM in 1952 (but not in his sleep). He noticed through research that at points during our sleep our eyes flutter underneath our eyelids (eye say!). He continued his research, and discovered in REM we dream most vividly (eye wonder what he dreamed about?).

DSM-IV

DSM-IV stands for the Diagnostic and Statistical Manual. It's an American publication and used by most mental health professionals to help identify and diagnose different types of mental illness.

It's a massive book that gets updated each decade (at the moment we're on Version 4 – great bedtime reading or doorstop!)

The first edition was published in 1952 by the American Psychiatric Association, and the next one's due out in 2012 (just in time for the London Olympics and the madness that will create!).

It's the book professionals use to define mental illness; it's full of terms that describe symptoms and conditions to do with the mind.

Whilst it's crucial as a frame of reference, some might argue that the diagnostic terms have created boxes to put people on or labels to describe someone.

Nevertheless, it's the mental health bible listing all the conditions we can experience and once we know what we've got we can soon start our treatment programme and/or path to recovery.

"We're all crazy…the only difference between patients and their therapists is the therapists haven't been caught yet."
Max Walker

E

ECT or Electroconvulsive therapy

Although there's evidence that the Romans were the first to use ECT (they used electric eel shocks as a headache cure). ECT, as we know it today, was invented during the 1930s.

Italian physicians Ugo Cerletti and Lucio Bini developed ECT after watching the effect of electric shocks on pigs before slaughter. Cerletti noticed that after the shock, pigs became calmer. If left to live, they completely recovered. (Shocking!)

Cerletti performed his first ECT treatment in April 1938. The first male patient, known as SE, was admitted to hospital by the police commissioner of Rome and diagnosed by Cerletti with schizophrenia. SE received a charge of 80 volts of electricity for 0.2 seconds, and it's said his body jumped and stiffened, but he awoke singing!

Today, ECT is amongst the most controversial modern psychiatric treatments but can be life-saving.

It's used in extreme cases of depression when all other treatments have failed. It's also affective in treating new mums with postpartum psychosis, a severe but rare mood disorder. It is also used to treat severe schizophrenia postnatal depression and also catatonia. If it works, the effects of ECT are noticed very quickly.

The use of ECT requires rigorous health checks and procedures; the treatment involves passing a controlled electrical current through the brain, which causes the body to have a seizure (a fit). ECT takes place under a general anaesthetic; muscle relaxants are also used to reduce the effects on the body.

Although ECT has been used for some 70 years, no one knows precisely how it works. It's believed to deaden brain activity so has significant risks attached to it which makes it so controversial. The Royal College of Psychiatrists has published a book with more details and guidelines.

Educational psychologists

A child comes home from his first day at school.

Mum asks, "What did you learn today?"

The child replies, "Not enough. I have to go back tomorrow."

“Educational psychologists tackle problems encountered by young people ineducation. This may involve learning difficulties and social or emotional problems. They carry out a wide range of tasks with the aim of enhancing children's learning and enabling teachers to become more aware of the social factors affecting teaching and learning.”
British Psychological Society

Most educational psychologists are employed by local authorities and work in schools, colleges, special units and nurseries. They work mostly with teachers and parents.

Sometimes educational psychologists work directly with young people or indirectly within the systems that support them.

Educational psychologists carry out assessments of some young people to explore where the problems lie. Once they’ve made an assessment, they put together interventions and treatment programmes to improve a young person’s situation while learning.

Educational psychologists are often used to advise others who work with children and young people. They help develop and devise policies, and may also carry out research in their field.

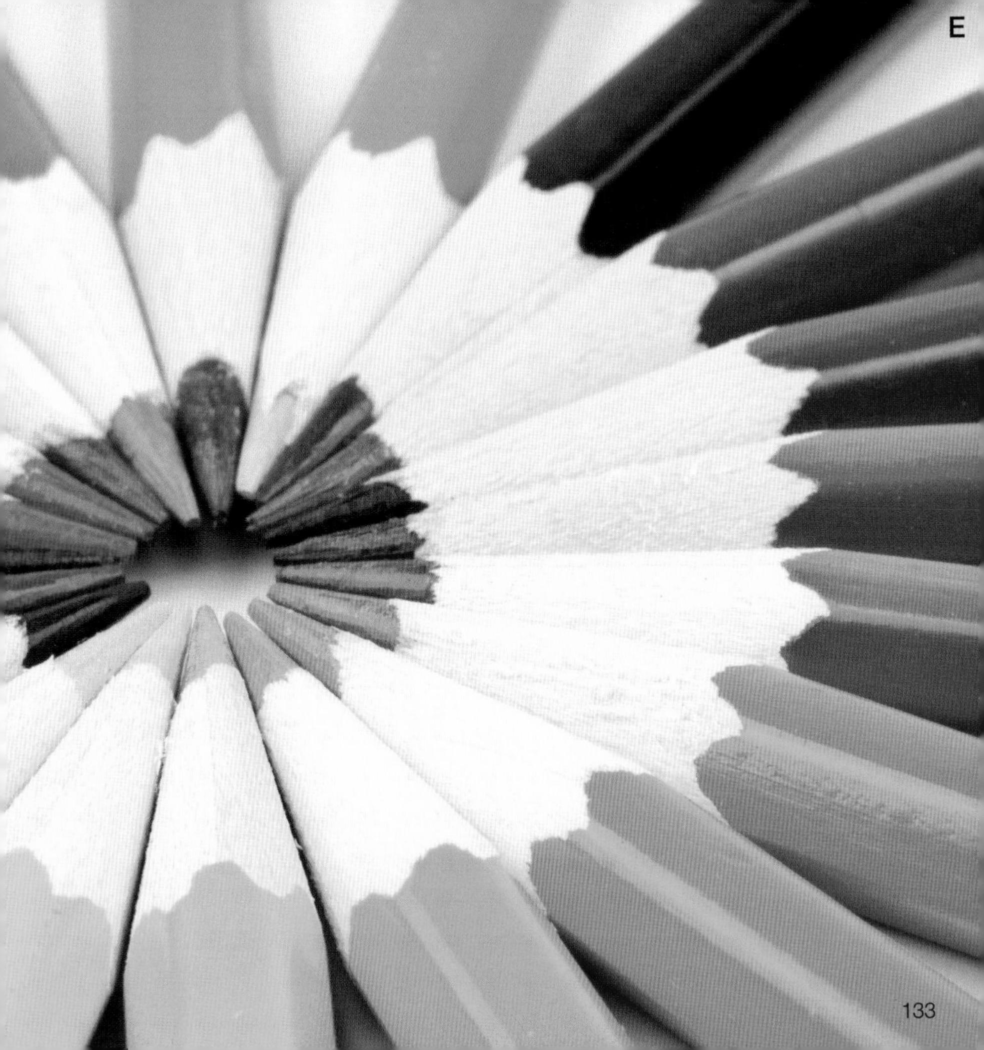

Ego

Ego is Latin for "I myself".

Sigmund Freud was the first to use the term "ego" or "das Ich" to explain part of our mind and personality. The ego is the part of the mind we know as I or me, the part that's in touch with reality. Our ego exists through our conscious mind and creates individuality of thought.

Freud believed that our personality is made up of three "psychic" parts: the id, the ego and the superego (see pp.188,334).

Our ego manages our internal drives and impulses: aggression, libido and our perceived need for food and safety. Our ego makes sense of the external world and informs our perception of reality. It's in charge of how we see things and how we adapt to the world as we experience it.

Our ego sits between our id and superego. Our id is the part of our mind that wants our needs met; it creates all our feelings (and won't take no for answer). Our superego applies values and opinions – either those we were taught, or one's we've developed. The ego sits between these two forces and needs to be healthy to manage them well.

A healthy ego means a healthy mind. If our ego is strong we can meet the needs of our id whilst managing the rules of our super-ego. Our ego applies logic and thought to events where our id provides drives and impulsion. The superego acts like our conscience, having both a critical and supportive function.

For Freud, our ego starts to develop in early infancy.

If life's a little bumpy during that time, it can affect how our ego develops. If our ego is strong, we can think through our problems, we can cope with the contradictions in life, and we can step back or engage.

But if our ego isn't healthy, life can be tough. We may find it hard to manage our feelings, make healthy decisions or think through our problems.

We may find it hard to be assertive or get our needs met without feeling guilty.

Psychotherapy can help us strengthen our ego and explore all the parts of our mind. As we begin to understand all the parts of our mind, our ego can develop and become stronger and more supportive.

Ego defence mechanisms

When the ego part of our mind is overwhelmed, it develops different kinds of defences. These are known as ego defence mechanisms.

Ego defence mechanisms help our mind cope, and they kick in as we experience high levels of stress and pressure, be it anxiety, sexual tension, fear, loss or aggression.

If we can't consciously think during an experience, the mind can distort the way we see things to protect our system from high levels of anxiety or painful feelings. Many of us experience the defence of "denial" when we can't believe someone close has died.

If we've inner conflict happening inside our heads, ego defences help, just the same.

We experience inner conflict when our instinctive drives and desires for pleasure, safety and survival clash with our internal values - the rules imposed or values we learned while small - that may no longer apply.

If we're taught while young that sex is shameful, we may attach those feelings to sexual desire. If we're taught that anger or aggression is bad, we can't use those drives to protect ourselves later, which sets us up for conflict within.

Our ego defences are mostly unconscious, so we don't realise we're using them. They're essential for the mind to cope under pressure but if we need them all the time our mind may need a little help.

There are 4 types of ego defences… here's a bit about them...

Pathological defence mechanisms. These types of ego defences interfere with our sense of reality. Sometimes we need them but if used all the time, they can harm both our mind and our body. Pathological defences include:

- **Denial:** our mind denies what's happening in reality to avoid anxiety or painful feelings. The defence of denial is most common when we lose a loved on.
- **Distortion:** our mind distorts reality so we can cope with it.
- **Delusion:** our mind creates a false reality inside our head to protect us from the real reality.

Immature defence mechanisms. These defences develop in childhood and although we tend to outgrow them, we may use them later as adults. Immature defences include:

- **Projection:** our mind attributes our unacknowledged feelings onto others including love, fear, jealously or anger.
- **Passive aggression:** our mind experiences aggression toward someone or something but expresses it indirectly, often in unhealthy ways.
- **Fantasy:** our mind retreats to a fantasy world because we feel it's better than facing reality; we fulfil our wishes and desires in the world of heads rather than in the world around us (sexual fantasies spring to mind!).

Neurotic defences. These defences are common to all of us but can get in the way of healthy relationships if we use them all of the time. Neurotic defences include:

- **Repression:** our mind holds back or subdues feelings or desires that seem unacceptable or we don't want to face.
- **Reaction Formation:** our mind makes us do the opposite of what we want or feel or need, being overly nice to someone we dislike, taking care of someone when we need care ourselves.
- **Displacement:** our mind directs particular feelings away from the intended target on to a safer one. Instead of being angry with our boss,we get angry with our partner or dog!

Mature defences. A healthy mind adopts mature defences to help cope with the conflicts of our thoughts and feelings. They help us live life more effectively:

- **Altruism:** when we give service to others for our own satisfaction.
- **Humour:** when we joke about something that's actually painful as a way to discharge our discomfort – if we work as a soldier or in the emergency services, we may use jokes to deal with events.
- **Sublimation:** when we channel unacceptable desires or feelings through an acceptable form – we hit a punch bag (rather than a person!).
- **Suppression:** when we consciously put a thought or feeling aside so we can deal with our present reality, knowing we can come back to it later.

"Child abuse casts a shadow the length of a lifetime." Herbert Ward

Emotional abuse

The term emotional abuse covers a wide and far-reaching range of behaviour that undermines, hurts and violates others. It's a form of abuse that's incredibly pervasive. It takes place at home, at school and at work, and through all sectors of society, and is often ignored. Though the scars are less visible, it hurts all the same.

Emotional abuse is when others control, manipulate, humiliate, violate, invalidate or disrespect our emotional state and psychological boundaries. Instead of physical harm, emotional abuse hurts our heads and our hearts.

Emotional abuse happens all the time. We may have experienced it as children or be experiencing it as an adult right now. We get punched with words or punished with silence.

Emotional abuse is verbal or psychological. Being ignored or shunned is just as painful, and all part of this form of abuse. From being rejected by caregivers to being shamed by our teachers to being bullied at work as an adult, emotional abuse happens to many of us every day and is the cause of great pain and trauma.

Emotional abuse affects our mind. It hurts and distorts our reality. We may develop anxiety, depression or insomnia as a response to being abused in this way. Emotional abuse affects our self-esteem, and it damages confidence and our trust in others.

Emotional abuse is part and parcel of physical and sexual abuse; it's often thought that it's the emotional aspect that causes people most harm.

There are many organisations and therapists who can support us if we've experienced this abuse or it's happening right now. They're listed at the back of this book.

Affirmation: I have the power to change my life at any moment.

Emotions

"Any emotion, if it is sincere, is involuntary." Mark Twain

Emotions are mental, physical and biological states that form and inform our response system.

We don't always knowingly create our emotions but we can learn how to change our emotional responses.

The word "emotion" originates from the Latin word "exmovere", meaning to move; the French word "émotion" means excitement (and the British for emotion is stiff upper lip!).

Emotions develop as we come into contact with external stimuli; they're formed by electrochemical reactions in the brain that help us make sense of our external environment.

Some of our emotions are created by thoughts – our memories carry emotional responses and as we recall them we re-experience the emotion.

We're capable of experiencing a range of emotions but happiness, sadness, anger and fear are the core, authentic feelings at the heart of humanity.

Our fight and flight emotions protect our minds and our bodies, our gladness and sadness build the bonds of community.

Emotions protect and connect us (as long as we let them).

"When dealing with people, remember you are not dealing with creatures of logic, but creatures of emotion." Dale Carnegie

“Human behaviour flows from three main sources: desire, emotion and knowledge.” Plato

Empathy

"The great gift of human beings is that we have the power of empathy."
Meryl Streep

Empathy is different to sympathy: sympathy is feeling with, empathy is feeling into. It comes from the concept of Einfühlung – the ability to comprehend someone's state rather than actually experiencing it.

We use empathy when we imagine other people's experiences as they might see them whilst suspending the world of our own.

"Friendship is a living thing that lasts only as long as it is nourished with kindness, empathy and understanding."
Mary Lou Retton

Empathy is about a shared experience where we see the world from another's view without judgement, advice or concern.

Empathy is key in unlocking understanding, a powerful part of any process of change.

As we feel understood, we can understand ourselves and begin to understand others.

When we experience empathy we don't feel alone, we feel the hand of another as we walk through our world.

It's a core condition for any person-centred counsellor (someone we can talk to if we're in need of empathy).

"You never really understand a person until you consider things from his point of view . . . until you climb inside of his skin and walk around in it." Atticus Finch. From Harper Lee's To Kill a Mockingbird.

Existential therapy

Existential therapy developed in Europe during the 1920s: it was introduced to Great Britain by Dr R D Laing.

This type of talking therapy explores and is informed by existentialism, a philosophical theory that looks at existence. What does it mean to exist?

Existential (and extinct!) thinkers have informed this philosophy: Aristotle, Socrates, Nietzsche and Sartre have all informed existential theory and many continue to today.

Existential therapy asks as to explore what life means to us…

What does it mean to be alive?

What are the possibilities my life presents me with?

What do I value and cherish?

What is my relationship to myself, others, the world around me?

What is the nature of the anxiety I experience in my life?

What would it be like to choose my own way of living?

As we reflect upon some of these fundamental questions, we may find it easier to understand our problems and challenges by putting them into a different context or seeing them from a different angle.

Life isn't always what we expect…

"Expect nothing and gain everything." Darren Bottrill

Extroverts and Introverts

The term "extrovert" was (along with "introvert") coined by Dr Carl Jung (1875–1961) to describe two types of character traits.

Extrovert describes someone who tends to be very outgoing.

If we're an extrovert, we channel our energy outwardly into our physical and social world. We quickly get bored of spending time by ourselves and prefer the company of others.

Extrovert types tend to be louder and bubblier, and our gratification comes from the world outside rather than the world within. The teaching, performing and other social professions attract extroverts.

An introvert is the opposite of an extrovert (funny that!).

If we're introverted, we tend to keep our energy inside ourselves, we prefer our own company and we are content with solitude. We generally have a smaller group of friends and prefer more intimate activities – writing, reading and drawing or painting. Artists, writers and sculptors tend to be introverts, prefering time in their own company.

“For an introvert his environment is himself and can never be subject to startling or unforeseen change”.

Quentin Crisp

F

Family therapy

Family therapy is similar to relationship counselling with highly qualified and experienced practitoners. A family therapist can help us explore how we interact as a family and find better ways of relating and living together.

Our emotional wellbeing is often associated with relational difficulties. Close relationships can fuel problems and sometimes they can break down under strain. Equally, our close relationships can also be important to recovery and a way to improve our lives.

Family therapy aims to maximise the strength of the family and family members. It can also be useful for other groups of people who care about each other and wish to improve their relationships.

Family therapists are trained to work with adults and children, they can help with all kinds of family concerns: mental health difficulties, self-harm, ADHD, trauma, eating disorders, bereavement, anger, addiction, divorce and domestic violence, as well as family illness, child and adolescent behavioural problems, step-family issues, fostering, adoption and the needs of "looked after" children.

Family therapy can be accessed through our GP or health visitor, they can refer us or family therapists working privately will be registered with either the BACP or UKCP.

AFT, the Association of Family Therapists has a list of registered family therapists and more information about family therapy.

Fear

Doctor, Doctor, I fear I'm turning into an apple.

Don't worry, we'll soon get to the core of this!

Fear is a core, authentic feeling. We experience fear in the present moment – it arises as a warning signal and is caused by the chemical adrenaline.

In the days of sabretooth tigers and cave dwelling, the feeling of fear enabled the human race to survive. Today we experience fear as anxiety – anxiety is diluted or unreleased fear.

"There is nothing to fear except the persistent refusal to find out the truth, the persistent refusal to analyze the causes of happenings."
Dorothy Thompson

The feeling of fear is helpful to us, because it motivates us to avoid or take action. Fear is attached to specific dangers, be they people, events or life situations.

Experiencing fear can make us do something in response. The experience of anxiety, diluted fear, doesn't always promote action – and inaction can cause it, as well.

Being in touch with our sense of fear is useful to us; it can guide us about what's safe and what isn't.

If we experience the feeling of fear and anxiety all the time, it might be worth exploring our situation with a counsellor or therapist. We all have the capacity to feel safe and secure in life.

"It's not that I'm afraid to die, I just don't want to be there when it happens."
Woody Allen

Affirmation: It's okay to feel fear. I support and take care of myself when I feel fearful.

F

Feelings

Feelings are physical sensations; they are our body's response to emotion, surroundings and what we do with ourselves. When we feel happy, sad, angry or sexually aroused we experience sensations in our body. Our sensations put us in touch with our emotions and influence what we do – how we act, how we move, the words we choose to say and the way we choose to say them.

Our feelings are influenced by the way that we think, so if we're thinking unhappy thoughts they can create the emotion of sadness and we may cry. Experiencing and sharing our feelings is good for the mind, because it helps us state where we're at and releases their energy. But if we bottle feelings up, having to spend the energy we use to do this means we can become depressed or anxious.

Feeling, like thinking or doing, is a state of awareness; when we are feeling we are being.

Feelings are physical but also emotional – they make us the individuals that we are; feelings are evoked as we experience events or what others say or do.

Experiencing our feelings and expressing them gives us meaning and a way to connect. As we share our true feelings we can feel close and supported, (depends on who we talk to, though!) and sharing and being aware of our feelings helps understanding.

We get taught how to censor and/or interpret our feelings by our parents or caregivers, which can make some feelings feel more acceptable than others. But whatever we've been taught, at times we may need to look at the ways we express and release our feelings (or not, as the case may be).

If we're in touch with our feelings and where they're coming from, we can protect them. If our feelings overwhelm us it can be hard to function, and we may need to explore why we find it hard to cope with them.

Fight/flight/freeze

Most living creatures have an in-built fight/flight/freeze response mechanism. In humans it's powered by our autonomic system, which is part of our nervous system – this means we don't consciously operate it. It's primitive and instinctive and kicks in when we are in danger or under threat, and it prepares our body to fight, run or stay very, very still (petrifying, really).

As this mechanism kicks in, rapid chemical reactions take place in our brain. Generally lots of adrenaline is released, making our heart beat faster and our breath quicken, so energy is released into our muscles and we become more alert, ready for appropriate action.

This mechanism saved humans when we lived in caves (alongside bears and sabretooth tigers) but today, it's pretty redundant except on the rare occasions we encounter extreme danger, emergencies, disasters or accidents.

The flight/fight response enables people to do amazing things, from hurdling a five-bar gate when chased by a bull to performing feats of heroism – during these moments we're not aware of our thinking, we just leap into action (quite literally at times).

For some of us, when stressed or under pressure, this system starts up, though we really don't need it. It causes extreme reactions to everyday things – it brings on any or all of panic attacks, aggression and a feeling of anxiety.

We can learn to train our response system – martial artists, military personnel and athletes use this mechanism to enhance what they do.

You know you're a martial artist if...when you trip, you go into a roll and come up in a fighting stance – in church!

F

F

Food and mood

The brain is a sophisticated factory that manufactures chemicals called neurotransmitters.

Neurotransmitters, such as serotonin, noradrenaline and dopamine, regulate our moods and emotions around the clock. As these neurotransmitters are themselves made up of nutrients found in food – amino acids, vitamins and minerals, what we eat can have a direct effect on how we think, feel and function.

Indeed, we can literally eat to *make* our hearts (and brains) content! Leading Nutritional Therapist Janine Fahri of NutriLife Clinic offers her expert tips on what to eat to help put a smile on our face and a spring back in our step.

The importance of blood-sugar balance

Blood-sugar balance is essential for a number of vital functions within the body including sustained energy levels, weight maintenance, stress management, brain function, and mood control.

How to help balance blood-sugar levels

- Eat regular meals and snacks- ideally every 3-4 hours. So, we need to have breakfast, a mid-morning snack, lunch, a mid-afternoon snack, and then dinner. The idea is that we have five smaller meals rather than three large ones – graze not gorge!

- Combine each meal and snack (including fruit) with a source of protein e.g. eggs, beans and pulses, lean chicken or turkey, low-fat cheese, fish, natural live yoghurt, nuts or seeds.

- Avoid alcohol, caffeine and sugar as these all wreak havoc with blood-sugar control. Furthermore, these are anti-nutrients whereby the body uses up vital vitamins and minerals when metabolising them.

- Avoid refined carbohydrates such as white bread and pasta. These quickly convert to glucose in the blood and typically result in energy slumps, anxiety, irritability, low mood, and high stress levels. Instead, opt for nutrient-dense whole-grains such as brown rice, whole-wheat pasta, oats, rye, and wholemeal bread.

Mood-boosting foods

The ingredients to a 'feel good' recipe are only a supermarket away!

Chicken and turkey contain a good source of tryptophan, an essential amino acid which is converted into serotonin aka the 'happy hormone'.

Specific vitamins and minerals are required to assist this conversion, so increase your intake of potatoes, bananas and lentils for vitamin B6; kidney beans and spinach for folic acid; papaya, broccoli and citrus fruit for vitamin C, and oysters for zinc.

Essential fatty acids (EFAs) perform myriad functions and are important for optimal brain function and can be helpful in alleviating depression. Good sources of EFAs include Brazil nuts, walnuts, pumpkin and sunflower seeds, avocados, oily fish (e.g. salmon, mackerel, anchovies, fresh tuna), and DHA-enriched 'intelligent' eggs.

Dietary supplements

Amino acids, vitamins, minerals, essential fats and certain herbs can be extremely beneficial to us. However, whilst the range on offer may resemble a "pick 'n' mix", dietary supplements are not sweeties! Seek professional advice.

Lab tests

Functional laboratory tests can be a valuable tool in determining any adrenal stress or fatigue, hormone imbalances, and food allergies/ intolerances.

For more information on all of the above, consult a Nutritional Therapist.

Sample mood-boosting menu

Breakfast

Wholemeal toast spread with nut butter and topped with a small chopped banana.

Mid-morning snack

Two oatcakes spread with humous. Serve with crudités such as mini carrot batons and celery sticks.

Lunch

Wholemeal pitta bread stuffed with organic skinless chicken, sliced avocado, and salad leaves lightly drizzled with olive oil.

Mid-afternoon snack

An apple combined with a handful of mixed, natural nuts.

Dinner

Fresh, organic wild salmon baked with lemon juice, fresh tarragon, and cracked pepper. Serve with new potatoes and a selection of steamed vegetables.

F
“Let medicine by thy food and food be thy medicine.” Hippocrates

Forgiveness

Though not available through our doctors or pharmacists, forgiveness is free and it's stored in our hearts. Forgiveness, like compassion, can help ease our mind. We can apply it to people or painful events, it helps us heal hurts or re-hashing the past, and it sits alongside acceptance.

"When a deep injury is done us, we never recover until we forgive." Alan Paton.

Often in life we can't control what happens, but we can control how we respond. Forgiving others for hurting our feelings, leaving this world or letting us down is a very empowering and healing action. When we forgive we let go of the past, and then the part of us that hurts can soon heal. As we forgive we release painful feelings and can fill up on the future instead.

"Always forgive your enemies - nothing annoys them so much." Oscar Wilde

But first we must completely forgive ourselves for the mistakes that we've made or any harm we've caused, whether or not it was our intention at the time. We can heal ourselves with our own forgiveness. Only then will we be able to forgive others.

"Forgiveness is a funny thing. It warms the heart and cools the sting." William Arthur Ward

The best-selling author Louise Hay links resentment to cancer, and she believes forgiveness is a quality that can help cure it – she had terminal cervical cancer and made a complete recovery.

"Forgiveness does not change the past but it does enlarge the future."

Paul Boese

Frame of reference

When all you've got is a hammer, everything looks like a nail!

Each of us has a unique "frame of reference"; it's a term coined by Transactional Analysis therapist Jacqui Schiff (1970) to define the way we each experience reality, our sense of what's real, true or false.

Our frame of reference is formed and learned in childhood, and includes our values, beliefs and assumptions about ourselves, others and the world around us. It's a bit like a pair of glasses: sometimes they help us to see things more clearly, but sometimes they tinge or colour our view.

If we're told, while we're small, that the world's unsafe, it's likely that as we grow we'll see it that way. If as children we're told we're "bad" or "good", that will affect our self-regard later.

Early lessons and the view of others we've been taught colour our experience of life. Most of the time what most of us learned was helpful, but some early lessons warp what we see in ourselves and others, and what we feel life is about.

Our frame of reference is part of our mind. It governs how we think, feel and act. If our mind is healthy, happy and positive, it's likely we'll see life and ourselves in this way. And if our mindset is negative or has been distorted by others, this too will affect our life, just the same.

We're not always aware we've been taught how to see life, but just as we learn we can unlearn too. If we want life to be different – happier and healthier – we may need our mind to change its perceptions.

By owning, exploring and accepting our view we can soon learn to change it and see what we want.

Games (psychological)

Game theory was developed by Eric Berne, founder of Transactional Analysis (TA).

We all play games; they help reinforce our "frame of reference" (see over). We do it when we've an ulterior motive that we're either unaware of or don't want to declare! Most psychological games are unhealthy, but some are fun – depends on how everyone involved feels at the outcome.

Games are usually outdated ways to get our needs met. We often resort to them without thinking, and they often lead to confusion or harm. Games are a series of communication moves that have a "snare" at the end – vocal manoeuvres rather than honest requests.

Games mostly start with a discount, a denial of our needs or the needs of others. If we need recognition we may put ourselves down, in the hope that another will say something nice.

Rather than just saying "I need recognition", we use a game as a way to get it … and when we don't get it, 'cause we haven't asked clearly, we feel worse or blame others, so everyone ends up feeling bad.

The opposite of a game is an "operation" – an explicit request that has a specific purpose and results in needs being met. If we ask openly for support and it's something we get, then games cease to take place.

Games are played as a way to avoid intimacy, both within ourselves and with other others around us. If we value our needs and those of others around us, we can work towards giving and receiving, without needing to play games.

Genuineness

"There is something in every one of you that waits and listens for the sound of the genuine in yourself. It is the only true guide you will ever have. And if you cannot hear it, you will all of your life spend your days on the ends of strings that somebody else pulls." Howard Thurman

In ancient Rome, the word "genuine" meant to place on knees, originating from the custom of a new father declaring his son as his own by placing him on his knees (aaaah!).

Today, "genuine" means real, natural, and just as it is (and how often are we really real?).

Genuineness – authenticity or congruency as it's known – means us being our true self, being real and in the moment with both ourselves and others.

We're not always encouraged to be genuine and real. We're taught as children whether it's okay to be ourselves or not.

What we say or feel can get censored by others, so we develop a false self. As adults, we may hide our true feelings or censor our thoughts for fear of being rejected or disliked, or upsetting others. But genuineness is good for our heads and our hearts.

The more genuine we are with ourselves and others, the more genuinely we'll be received. And just as we are true to ourselves we allow others to be the same.

If we're genuine about our needs, our thoughts and feelings, others can respond the same way. Our relationships get closer, our needs can be met and our mind can feel calmer and more open.

"Learn to be quiet enough to hear the genuine within yourself so that you can hear it in others."
Marian Wright Edelman

For Carl Rogers, founder of Person-centred Therapy, congruence was one of the core conditions. It's at the heart of most therapeutic relationships, alongside empathy and unconditional positive regard.

By experiencing genuineness with or from a counsellor, we can begin to find and develop our own. As we become more authentic and accepting of ourselves, we don't need to adapt, play games or hide.

"Above all, be true to yourself, and if you cannot put your heart in it, take yourself out of it."
Hardy D. Jackson

Genuineness is about sharing what's in our hearts and our heads and that's just great for the mind.

"Accept everything about yourself. I mean everything. You are you and that is the beginning and the end - no apologies, no regrets"
Clark Moustakas

Gestalt therapy

“Gestalt” is a German word which means whole or to organise, or complete patterns.

Gestalt therapy was developed in the 1940s by Fritz and Laura Perls. It is one of the humanistic psychotherapies, alongside Existential and Person-centred.

In this, a type of talking therapy, Gestalt therapists encourage us to focus on the present moment and develop more authentic ways of relating. This can improve our own sense of self, our relationships and what we bring to our experiences.

Gestalt therapy recognises the uniqueness of every individual, that we’re each made up of mind, body and spirit. As individuals, we can only be really understood in relation to our situation as we ourselves experience it. The need of any moment creates the field by which we deal with it.

At the core of Gestalt therapy is the promotion of personal responsibility and self-awareness.

As a therapy, it encourages us to be non-judgemental and real about what we are experiencing moment by moment – all of our feelings, perceptions, sensations and actions, and how we meet our needs, from eating to intimacy.

As we begin to experience ourselves as we respond to our world in the here and now, we can begin to recognise old patterns and change them by completing past or unresolved experiences from within.

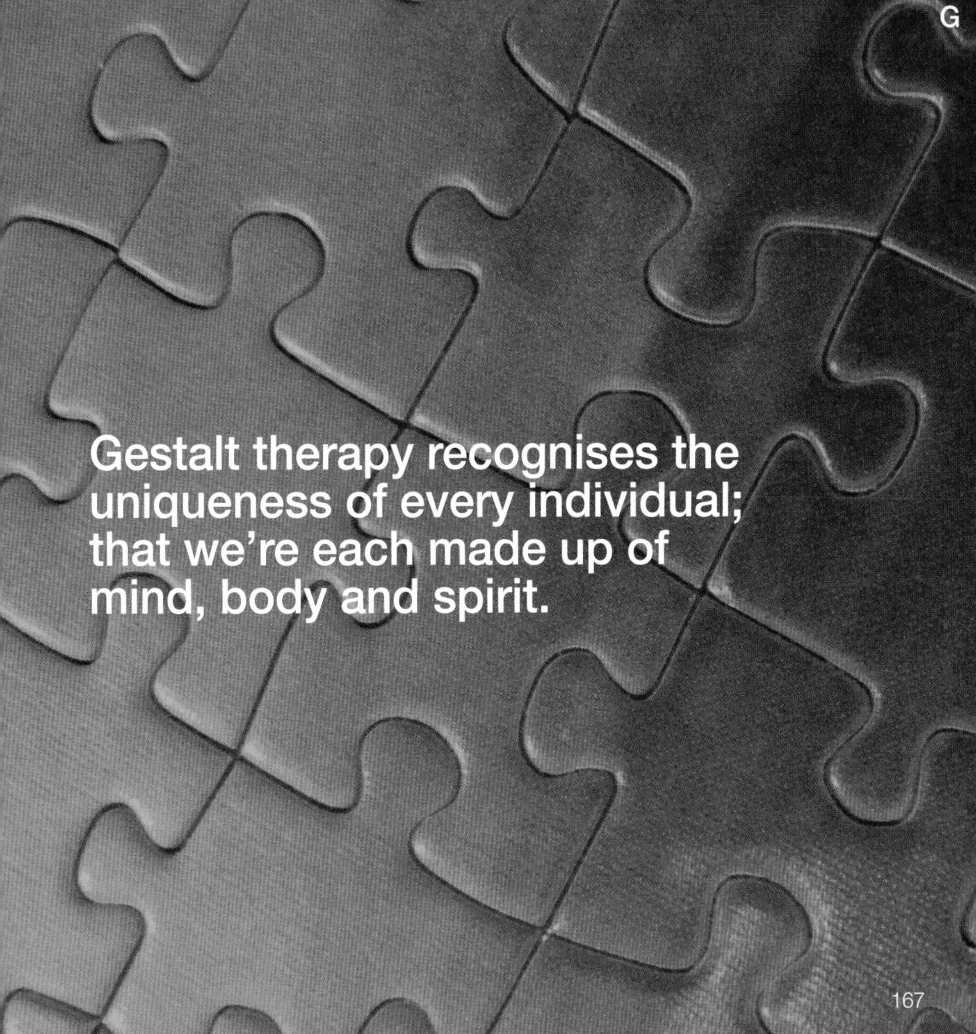

Gestalt therapy recognises the uniqueness of every individual; that we're each made up of mind, body and spirit.

Gratitude

Rather than cursing life events or others who have harmed or hurt us, we can choose to be grateful for the challenging experience which allows us to grow from these things and opens our mind to opportunity.

"Gratitude unlocks the fullness of life. It turns what we have into enough, and more. It turns denial into acceptance, chaos to order, confusion to clarity. It can turn a meal into a feast, a house into a home, a stranger into a friend. Gratitude makes sense of our past, brings peace for today, and creates a vision for tomorrow." Melody Beattie

Life indeed has its ups and downs. We can learn from mistakes and be grateful for the gifts or we can choose to feel sorry or grumpy (depends on our state of mind).

Things are either positive or negative, just depends how we see them. If we see them as negative, we can change our mind and choose to see gifts - every cloud has a silver lining - we just have to look for it sometimes.

Is your glass half full or half empty?

If we've had a breakdown, depression, addiction or loss, we may find it hard to accept, but if we choose to use gratitude and learn from our experiences, we can grow and develop our minds. Many people who've experienced hard times look back with more strengths and insights: overcoming tough times can be the making of us (my tricky times have led to this book).

"Develop an attitude of gratitude, and give thanks zfor everything that happens to you, knowing that every step forward is a step toward achieving something bigger and better than your current situation." Brian Tracy

"Gratitude is when memory is stored in the heart and not in the mind." Lionel Hampton

Grief

"He that conceals grief finds no remedy for it."

Grief is an intense feeling of sorrow experienced in response to a major loss – at the death of a loved one, at the end of a significant relationship or divorce.

According to Mind, 1 in 4 of us has experienced the death of a loved one in the last 5 years.

Experiencing grief and allowing ourselves to do so is important to the health of our mind. Experts believe if we don't grieve properly these big emotions stay locked up inside and can lead to physical or emotional difficulties later (they catch us up sooner or later).

We all grieve in different ways; grief helps us come to terms with our loss and the changes in our bonds of attachment.

Grieving takes time. There is no fixed route or timescale to grief, but there can be different and overlapping stages to it.

At first we can feel numb, shocked or devastated by the event. We may experience denial, finding it hard to believe a loved one has passed or that we're facing a serious illness.

As we come to terms with the news, we may feel an intense yearning, a desperate need to see that person again, or we may still want to see and be with them (or continue to be with them for longer).

At times we may feel angry, agitated, unable to sleep or relax, and we may feel regret, or even guilt, over things we did or didn't do or say.

At some point we'll feel an intense sense of sadness. We may need to withdraw and spend time alone, and give ourselves silence and time to be quiet.

Gradually, with time, we can work through these stages; we may need to go back and forth between them, but then, as soon as we're ready, we'll find a sense of acceptance and we'll be able carry on with our lives, though that person's not with us, not part of our life.

Grief affects the mind, it's a process that involves both our head and our heart. If we're prone to depression or are vulnerable emotionally, grief can be harder to cope with.

Experiencing a major loss can be an extremely painful experience, one that we'll each have to face at some point or another. The process of grieving our loss is an important part of overcoming our loss and moving on.

At times, we may find it helpful to share our grief confidentially, we may find it helpful to talk to a bereavement counsellor or someone trained in this specific part of life.

Organisations such as Cruse Bereavement Care can help us find support, their details are listed at the back of the book.

Grounding

When we're grounded we're in touch with our full self, our connection to our body, our senses and the outside world around us.

We can feel our feet on the floor and we're aware of our body, our breath, how we feel and can experience our thoughts in an observational way rather than getting caught up in them.

When we are grounded we're in the here and now, more able to experience happiness and fulfilment – but if we're ungrounded we're more likely to feel fear, sadness and anxiety.

Ken Mellor developed one of the first grounding techniques. They help to centre our mind and release emotion through our physical body, giving us time to find our own natural state.

We need to give ourselves time to ground, and we can do it lying, sitting, standing up (even while we're driving and during sex!).

Grounding ourselves is simple...

We can start by focusing on our feet – the sensations and feelings of our shoes or socks – then gradually we move our awareness up through our body, our bits and our bum, our back and our front and up through our face to our head.

We can take some deep breaths and begin to feel our whole body in the moment and the sensations we are getting from the world around us; are we hot or cold, what can we hear or smell?

When we're grounded we can observe and experience without getting caught up in sensations. We can begin to notice where we're holding tension or what the thoughts are that we have in our minds.

If things have made us angry or sad, we can think those thoughts as we ground our bodies, which helps us let go of these emotions. Then, as we release our emotions, we can think more calmly.

Group analysis

"Three groups spend other people's money: children, thieves and politicians, all three need supervision!"
Dick Army

Siegfried Foulkes (1898–1976) was the first to develop and practise group analysis. As a trained psychotherapist, he ran his first psychotherapy group in Exeter, in Devon, in 1939. His groupwork with WW2 veterans led to him set up the Group Analysis Society in 1952 and The Institute of Group Analysis in 1971; they're based in London today.

Foulkes believed that groups are basic to human existence; they give us a sense of belonging. He explored group dynamics and how we all operate as individuals and as part of a group, the roles we assume and the way we relate.

Group analysis is a form of therapy. It can help us improve our relating skills, and it can also give us confidence and improve our esteem as we learn to share or extend support to others.

Group therapy is also helpful if we're feeling anxious or are coming to terms with a loss.

When we're part of a therapy group, we can experience and grow through the support of others. As we open up and share our feelings or problems, we can learn from others that we're far from alone.

Effective group analysis is run by trained group analysts. There are usually eight other members, and sessions tend to take place weekly for an hour, but it will vary from group to group.

"Individual commitment to a group effort - that is what makes a team work, a company work, a society work, a civilisation work."
Vince Lombardi

Guilt

"Food, love, career and mothers, the four major guilt groups !!!" Cathy Guisewite

Guilt is a feeling triggered by our conscience, our sense of what's right or wrong. When we've conflict inside because we have or haven't done something we should, we tend to feel guilty.

Guilt is about our actions, and shame is about who we are.

Guilt affects our mind. If we feel guilty inside we can be hard on ourselves, we may feel we're unworthy or undeserving of good things, and this can lead to depression and low self-esteem.

If we feel guilty all the time, we may feel over-responsible, want to make everything right or be overly giving. We may find it hard to make choices for ourselves because we've been taught to put others first.

If we put others first, we allow what they do or say to give us guilt feelings, and that kind of guilt is a glue that sticks – it can hurt and harm us and control what we do.

Most of us know what a guilt trip's like (it ain't no holiday, that's for sure!).

If they choose to, people can manipulate our sense of guilt to trigger us into doing things, staying with them or supporting them – even if we really don't want to.

Very often it's the people who experience guilt who are the ones to dish it out.

They use a certain tone of voice or reflect to us our own words or actions, triggering us into feeling responsible for something when it's really they who are. Or, they manipulate us into us feeling responsible for them being in the place that they're in rather than taking on that responsibility themselves.

Our experience of guilt can be attached to old beliefs and things we were taught while we were young.

We may have learned that…

…we do not deserve to feel happy

…we're responsible for everyone else's happiness

…it's wrong to put ourselves first

... it's bad to feel feelings of hurt

…what others think of us is significant or important

…everyone is judging us and their judgments are important

…we should always be giving to others.

And we're even taught to believe we shouldn't feel guilty!

On the upside, not all guilt is bad, it can be very motivating.

Sometimes, we're not aware of the amount of guilt that we hold – it's a feeling we repress into our unconscious mind.

But, it still influences how we feel about ourselves, others in our life and our sense of self-worth. People with low self-esteem are more likely to experience guilt.

We can explore our feelings of guilt by talking to a counsellor or therapist. As we become aware of the beliefs we've been taught, we change them, replacing them with our own set of values. As we develop a stronger sense of self and become more responsible for ourselves we can set new boundaries that support and protect us.

"I have never smuggled anything in my life. Why, then, do I feel an uneasy sense of guilt on approaching a customs barrier?" John Steinbeck

Affirmation: I release the need to feel guilty; I can protect myself from the ways of others.

Hallucinations

Doctor, Doctor...I keep seeing double!

Please sit on the couch!

Which one???

Hallucinations are about what we perceive. When they happen in our mind, we may hear voices in our head and adopt strange, unusual or unfounded beliefs, or our thoughts may just leap around.

With hallucinations, we may feel paranoid, as if people are bugging our phones or watching us. We may experience delusions of grandeur where we believe we are related to God or the queen.

Hallucinations can be very disturbing. It can be frightening to experience our mind wandering off, and it can be distressing for the people around us.

Many things cause hallucinations, including lack of sleep, illegal drugs or illnesses like malaria.

Most of us who've hallucinated never have one again.

Some delusions can be because of a condition – we might be bipolar or schizophrenic and need diagnosis and treatment.

Antipsychotic drugs can help with hallucinations; they help restore the chemicals that support our perception, our sense of reality (see p.40).

It can be hard to share hallucinatory experiences because we fear people will think we are mad!

It can be helpful to talk through our experiences in a confidential space with a counsellor or support group; there we won't be judged or labelled.

H

Happiness

Keep a smile on your face. It would look funny anywhere else!

Happiness is our natural, grounded state. To feel glad is a core and authentic feeling.

Happiness is the feeling most associated with being present. If we wallow in the past we tend to feel sad, and if we think about the future we can also feel fear and/or anxiety.

Happiness is about being in the now, in the present; calm, centred and peaceful.

"The greatest part of our happiness depends on our dispositions, not our circumstances."
Martha Washington

Happiness is a state; we all have the capacity to feel happy all the time, and the more we are grounded through our mind and body, the more we feel happy.

Despite dramatic increases in our wealth and standards of living, research shows that our state of happiness is still just the same as it used to be (money, beyond having enough to cover the fundamentals of life – shelter, food, and warmth – really doesn't buy happiness).

Short-term happiness can come from things, but long-term happiness begins inside us. There are numerous stories about lottery winners whose lives have become miserable as a result of their wealth.

According to research carried out by Michigan University, Nigeria, Mexico, Venezuela, El Salvador and Puerto Rico are the top five happiest nations in the world. The UK is ranked 24th and the USA 16th!

"Happiness cannot
come from without.
It must come from
within" Helen Keller

So how can we become happier…if we think happy and behave happy chances are we will feel happy – here's a few suggestions...

1) We can get inside our body, spend a few minutes daily grounding ourselves. As we get in touch with our body, we centre our mind.

2) We can learn gratitude and appreciate what we've got rather than what we haven't – things, people, experiences and opportunities, the fact we're alive is a great place to start.

3) We can do more of what makes us happy, give ourselves more pleasure and happy times with others.

4) Smile – it makes us feel happy and tricks our mind to thinking it (fake it till you make it).

5) We can choose to give ourselves happy positive thoughts instead of negatives.

6) We can be optimistic: our thoughts create our feelings so let's think positive, we never know what lies ahead so let's feel excited about it.

7) We can learn to like ourselves and others. Think of 10 things that you like, value and appreciate about yourself and others everyday. Liking who we are is a good step towards loving and accepting ourselves.

8) Take more holidays. They tend to be the happiest experiences we have so let's have more of them!

9) We can develop new beliefs about ourselves and how we live that will support us in creating more happiness in our world.

10) Develop a sense of inner acceptance, that all is well and everything is as it should be.

5 secrets for women's romantic happiness...

1. It is important to find a man who works around the house, cooks and cleans and who has a job.

2. It is important to find a man who makes you laugh.

3. It is important to find a man who is dependable and doesn't lie.

4. It is important to find a man who's good in bed and who loves to have sex with you.

5. It is important that these four men never meet!

Hope

"Learn from yesterday, live for today, hope for tomorrow." Albert Einstein

Hope is an important feeling and a quality we may need if we're facing hard times or hardship. Hope gives us the sense that things will get better; by giving ourselves hope, we can have confidence that we'll get through.

The more we feel happy and are grounded in the moment, the less we need hope as it's linked to the future, but hope can still help us.

Hope is good for our heads. We can't predict the future or control what's coming, but if we're hopeful and happy we can feel much more positive about what lies ahead. If we believe there's a light at the end of the tunnel, we're much more likely to find it.

Hope enables us to approach adversity in a positive way. It gives us strength and courage, and keeps our mind looking forward!

"Hope arouses, as nothing else can arouse, a passion for the possible."
William Sloane Coffin Jnr.

If we've experienced anxiety or depression, hope is a hard thing to find. It takes determination and grit to hope when we feel hopeless, but finding it is essential to healing our heads.

"The most important things in the world have been achieved by people who have kept on trying, even when there seemed to be no hope at all." Dale Carnegie

As we begin to develop a sense of all being well in the here and now, the less we need hope. Hope fuels the future, and happiness fills the present.

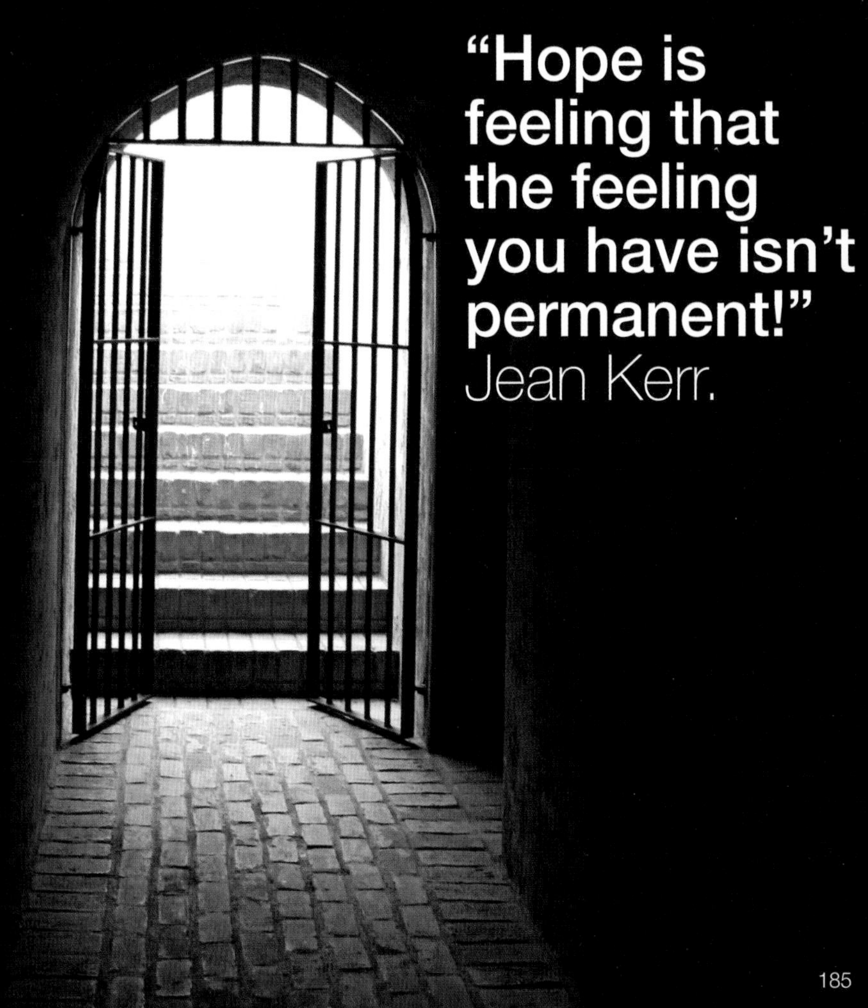

"Hope is feeling that the feeling you have isn't permanent!"
Jean Kerr.

Hypnotherapy

Dr Franz Anton Mesmer was one of the first physicians to use and develop mesmerisation – what we know today as hypnosis.

Hypnotherapists believe that the unconscious mind is more powerful than the conscious one. Through hypnosis, with a trained and qualified professional, we are invited to go into a deep trance-like state of relaxation where we bypass our conscious mind and so can access our unconscious.

While we're in this state, a hypnotherapist can give suggestions and ideas, and talk directly to our unconscious, which can help to reprogramme our mind. It can bring about change, help us overcome fear or kick habits or addictions.

Hypnotherapy can provide short-term results; any benefits from this type of treatment will be noticed after one or a few sessions.

It is helpful for people who experience phobias, anxiety, stress or trying to give up smoking.

Some of us fear hypnotism as we think we're not in "control". This is not usually the case, but it's important to trust the hypnotherapist we choose and ensure we feel safe and comfortable with them.

Clearly, if we're allowing someone else to influence us in this way it's extremely important that we choose someone whose ethics are beyond reproach and whose outlook on life matches our idea of how we would like ours to be.

The word "mesmerise" comes from the name of an eighteenth century physician, Dr Franz Anton Mesmer.

Id

The term "id" was coined by Sigmund Freud to describe the most instinctive part of our mind. Our id resides in the unconscious and conscious part of our mind.

The id part of us holds our instincts; it's where our drive for survival and pleasure exist.

Our id drives our basic need for warmth, food, sex and pleasure.

It's the part that won't take No for an answer – newborn babies are essentially all id, and their ego doesn't develop till age three or over.

The id part of our mind is disorganised – it's without a frame of reference, it's a psychic energy source that drives the rest of our mind to get what we want.

Freud believed that the id part of us is the source of our libido – our sex drive (interesting id-ea!)(see p.209).

In early childhood the id part of us follows what Freud called the Pleasure Principle, when we strive to avoid pain and only experience pleasure. (Some of us still do, but we're not complete id-iots!)

As we grow and mature, we learn that sometimes we have to endure a little pain; it's part of life and it's our path to healing.

"Where id was, there shall ego be."
Sigmund Freud

Identity and identity crisis

**Doctor, Doctor…
I think I'm a bell**

Take these and if it doesn't help give me a ring!

Our sense of identity is influenced and formed by our senses, the way we see ourselves, our sexual identity and the roles, characteristics, values and beliefs we've adopted.

If we have a strong identity, we know who we are, where we are coming from and why we do what we do. We feel confident in our world, and we can explore new roles and try things we haven't done before. We can support ourselves because we're confident inside.

"First say to yourself what you would be; and then do what you have to do."
Epictetus.

A strong identity enables us to be aware of our motivations – what makes us happy or sad, what we enjoy and what we value (our friends, partners, family, work, our hobbies and our own creativity).

With a strong identity, we feel a sense of belonging, both inside ourselves and in relation to the world. We know we're important and are part of a community and we feel empowered to bring about the changes we want, both in our lives and as part of a group.

With a strong identity we are able to flex and adapt to the demands of life – we're prepared for change and new avenues. We can take new risks and manage the consequences without feeling uncomfortably threatened.

Life events can challenge our identity. We may lose our job and feel disoriented, we may become parents and find it hard to cope, or we may become single again after a long-term relationship.

Affirmation: I am confident in all that I am and all that I can be.

At times we're unclear as to who we are or where we're heading, and perhaps that's when our journey begins.

Erik Erikson called this an "identity crisis", something most of us face during adolescence – as we break away from our family unit and begin to find our own way in the world. During this time we explore new roles and choose our own values and challenge the ideals of others.

Erikson believed an identity crisis to be one of the most important human conflicts in terms of personal development. If we're unsure of who we are and why we're here, we can begin to discover ourselves, entering a period of our life where we reflect, take stock and discover new qualities. We can soon adopt new values and commit to change, and with that we develop a stronger identity.

Research has shown that people who commit to and have a strong sense of identity tend to be more fulfilled and happy.

"A musician must make music, an artist must paint, and a poet must write, if he is to be ultimately at peace with himself. What a man can be, he must be."
Abraham Maslow

If we are experiencing an identity crisis or are unsure of where we're at, talking to a counsellor or therapist can help us we explore how we feel and find new meaning for ourselves.

"I can be an astronaut but I'm quite at peace here on earth!
Anon

Impasse

Impasse is a Transactional Analysis (TA) theory created by Mary and Robert Goulding in 1979 (see p.340).

The term "impasse" expresses how we sometimes become blocked or stuck in what we believe to be or experience as an irresolvable dilemma.

These dilemmas take place in our mind and body rather than in our outer reality, but they are often reflected in our own outer world.

We can experience impasse when our values or beliefs conflict with our desires and needs.

A part of us wants something physically or psychologically but another part of us tells us we can't have it.

It's a bit like being at loggerheads or deadlock within – resolution can't take place until one or the other gives way.

For the Gouldings, the way to resolve impasse is to explore our decision-making processes, what we learned as children that formed our framework for decisions.

Some of the decisions we made about ourselves and our lives in childhood interfere with our life as adults – and this is when we experience impasse.

But, by discovering and changing these decisions, we can release ourselves from our self-imposed entrapment.

Inferiority complex

"No one can make you inferior without your consent." Eleanor Roosevelt

We've all felt inferior at some point in life. We've looked up to others thinking they're better than us.

If we experience inferiority, or what's known as an inferiority complex, we feel inferior all the time. As we look around we think everyone is better, more talented than us, more capable or more popular than we can ever be … we may desperately want to be like all these people but tell ourselves we can't.

If we've an inferiority complex we automatically assume people are looking down on us, and that others think we are weak, unworthy or unattractive. We may feel frightened of others or find close relationships difficult, and we think people will reject us, or we place so much value on what they may think of us that this stops us doing things.

Thoughts of inferiority give rise to painful feelings such as despair, unworthiness, hopelessness and fear. We may feel angry, jealous or ashamed but our sense of inferiority carries on unabated.

Our sense of inferiority (or superiority) develops during childhood: it can be passed on from parents to children – if our parents felt inferior, it's likely we will too…

We may have felt intimidated because of the size of a parent or because of the way they expressed their anger.

They might have never acknowledged our strengths and talents, or told us we were good enough as we were.

We may have grown up feeling unimportant and insignificant to others, with no sense of self-worth.

As we reach adulthood, inferiority comes right along with us and gets in the way of our potential in life.

Those early lessons can limit our thinking and may have diminished our sense of what we're capable of, or what we can get from – and give to – life.

But we don't have to feel inferior; it's something we've learned and we can soon unlearn it.

If we want to change and release our potential, we can unlearn past lessons with a counsellor or therapist.

Each one of us is valuable; we're important in the greater scheme of things, just as each different cell in our own body is important to us. We are stronger than we know, a fount of resources. We've all got strengths and vulnerabilities and we've our own capabilities – but we may need to find them.

We're all different and we're all unique, and with time we can learn to celebrate that, strengthen our identity and grow in our self-worth.

"I would rather have an inferiority complex and be pleasantly surprised than have a superiority complex and be rudely awakened!"
Vanna Bonta

Affirmation: I like others am unique and valuable.

Injunctions and counter-injunctions

The term "injunction" was used by Mary and Robert Goulding (1972) to describe the early messages we take on board while we're young.

The messages we received from important others through hearing, seeing, feeling and unspoken communication were absorbed by our minds while we were small, and cemented as decisions.

Some messages were helpful, guiding us as to what was safe, helping us survive. Other messages informed us, for good or ill, of our value in the eyes of the senders, and how we "should" value ourselves, others and our world.

Injunctions are strong statements of self-worth that become decisions and beliefs; they teach us how to be, what to think and how to feel.

Whether they're appropriate or not, they can stick, but we can soon peel them off!

Injunctions are "don't" messages, like... Don't be who you are. Don't be close. Don't feel your feelings. Don't be successful. Don't be well (sane). Don't be important. Don't have needs or wants. Don't be good.

Injunction messages are often reinforced by "counter-injunctions" or "drivers", a term coined by Taibi Kahler. Counter-injunctions are behavioural manifestations of injunctions. They are a counter measure against the "don't" messages.

So alongside strong "don't" messages, adults can also give us powerful "do" messages like "hurry up", "be strong", "try hard", "be perfect" or "please others".

If we don't act in these ways, we don't feel accepted – we feel as though we're only okay as a person if we please, hurry or try hard. When injunctions and counter-injunctions are combined, they are particularly powerful.

One message tells us what not to do - “don’t be close” while the other tells us what to do instead - “be strong”.

Whilst drivers or counter-injunctions helped us (and those around us) cope while we were small, their traits remain in adulthood, when they may not be helpful to us. Injunctions and counter-injunctions distort our reality: how we see ourselves, others and what life has to offer.

As we become of how these messages have shaped us, we can soon learn how to shake them off.

With time, affirmations and perhaps help from a therapist, we can unlearn oland modes of behaviour, and strengthen our own natural state and sense of who we are.

“If you hear a voice within you say ‘you cannot paint’, then by all means paint and that voice will be silenced.”
Vincent Van Gogh.

Inner pain trauma

"Nothing lasts forever - not even your troubles." Arnold H. Glasgow

Inner pain trauma is caused by ungrieved loss, experiencing loss of intimacy and/or the death of a loved one. Loss or divorce can be the cause of a great deal of emotional distress and trauma.

"We are more often frightened than hurt; and we suffer more from imagination than from reality." Seneca

If we experienced loss in early childhood or have been unable to grieve past pain, it can hurt to love again because we may re-experience this pain as we attempt to heal it through another.

"Let your hopes, not your hurts, shape your future." Robert H. Schuller

If we hurt deep down and still haven't recovered, we may look to others to help heal our pain. We feel a hole deep within that we need to seal up, but we look to others or life to fill it.

"The hunger for love is much more difficult to remove than the hunger for bread." Mother Teresa

Holding on to inner pain trauma can create all or nothing thinking; each new opportunity, whether we're aware of it or not, becomes a place to be saved or to put things right, putting pressure on ourselves, others or events (see P.26).

"Hunger, love, pain, fear are some of those inner forces which rule the individual's instinct for self preservation." Albert Einstein

By our very nature, we are biologically driven to create bonds in relationships. Through these bonds we learn about love, care, nurture and intimacy.

Sometimes, when those bonds are broken a part of us snaps off, and in that trauma we lose a piece of ourselves. We then journey through life "hungry" for what's missing.

"The tragedy is not that a man dies, the tragedy of life is what dies inside a man while he lives."
Albert Schweitzer

Some believe inner pain trauma resides at the heart of most addictions; people drink or take drugs as inner pain relief.

If we don't let ourselves feel grief we build walls round our pain; if we don't let love in we can't heal and get better

Healing our hearts is good for our head; it strengthens our mind and enables us to trust life's process.

Nothing lasts forever – life's constantly changing – but as we recover and renew our bonds, we can develop new faith and trust in life's journey.

It takes courage to go back to unhealed wounds, but pain just gets greater if we pack it away.

"When you can't remember why you're hurt, that's when you're healed." Jane Fonda

A counsellor or therapist can give us support as we work through our hurts in a safe, caring space, and as we find these old holes, we can soon seal them up with the love we've found within.

Insomnia

"Sometimes I keep myself awake, worrying about not being able to sleep!"

Sleep is good for the mind.

Our brain is more active in sleep than when awake; we need rest and dream time to help our brain process our daily experiences or perhaps work through long-term things.

If we find it hard to sleep it can be a real nightmare! (Well not literally, 'cause we can't get to sleep, to have them!) The very fact we haven't slept can stress us out even more.

Generally, if our sleep pattern is interrupted through jet lag, a dog barking, noisy weather or worry it soon returns to normal, but sometimes it lasts much longer.

If so, we may need to talk to our doctor, but there are things that can help.

If we are poor sleepers, we find it hard to drop off, we wake extremely early or we wake in the middle of the night and lie there for what seems like hours (and probably is).

In the morning we feel far from refreshed, or we just feel tired most of the time.

One in five people have difficulty in sleeping.

We all need different amounts of sleep. A baby can need up to 17 hours per day – meanwhile, parents lose 450–700 hours of sleep while bringing up a new baby.

Most of us need around eight hours, and some feel okay on four hours a night (Margaret Thatcher had four hours a night while she was PM ... some people feel she needed 24 hours!)

The main thing to affect our sleep is our level of anxiety, making it hard to switch off at night.

Sometimes, we may experience the condition called apnoea, particularly if we're overweight – our air passages collapse, reducing the amount of oxygen we can breathe in, and waking us up.

Some prescribed drugs or stimulants such as coffee, nicotine and alcohol affect sleep.

Some people take sleeping pills to help them sleep but it's the underlying anxiety that needs to be treated.

If we can explore what's causing us to feel anxious and wired, we can sleep much better without needing pills!

Here's a few sleeping tips...

Learn some breathing and relaxation techniques to quiet the body and mind before dropping off to sleep.

Reduce caffeine, nicotine or alcohol – especially before bedtime.

Never sleep with another man's wife, you may never wake up!!!

Try and get into a routine: choose a regular time to go to bed.

Exercise regularly; allow a couple of hours between extreme exercise and bedtime (sex is okay though, a good rumble under the covers can soon tire us out!)

Avoid eating a heavy meal 4 hours before going to bed.

Never take a sleeping pill and a laxative on the same night!!!

Interdependency

"The person who tries to live alone will not succeed as a human being. His heart withers if it does not answer another heart. His mind shrinks away if he hears only the echoes of his own thoughts and finds no other inspiration." Pearl S. Buck

Interdependency describes a healthy co-existence with others, incorporating moments of dependence and independence.

"Let's face it. In most of life we really are interdependent. We need each other. Staunch independence is an illusion, but heavy dependence isn't healthy, either. The only position of long-term strength is interdependence: win/win." Greg Anderson

Interdependency is about balancing time with others and our time away. Sometimes we may need and want to be with people, and at others prefer our own company and space. If we're interdependent we want to be with others, if we're co-dependent we need to.

"In the progress of personality, first comes a declaration of independence, then a recognition of interdependence."
Henry Van Dyke

Intimacy

"My friends tell me I have an intimacy problem. But they don't really know me."
Garry Shandling

Intimacy is about being open with others and close to them from a personal place of authenticity.

In our intimate relationships we can be real and who we are, we can accept ourselves and we can accept others too, yet without trying to change or improve them!

In our intimate relationships we don't need to adapt or hide how we feel or what we think.

"Communication leads to community, that is, to understanding, intimacy and mutual valuing." Rollo May

When we're intimate with people, we can express authentic feelings; we might be intimately happy with one another but still can share anger or fear.

Eric Berne (1964) described intimacy as **"the spontaneous, game-free candidness of an aware person, the liberation of the eidetically perceptive [seeing things as they are], uncorrupted Child in all its naiveté living in the here and now."**

At times it can be hard to be intimate with people, especially if we're not intimate with ourselves. Intimate relationships involve trust, risk, authentic communication, patience and understanding.

Talking to a counsellor can help us with intimacy. As we share ourselves and feel accepted as they listen, we can begin to accept and be close to ourselves, and this can improve how we relate to others and how we relate within.

Affirmation: As I am intimate with myself I can be intimate with others.

Intuition

Doctor, doctor, I keep seeing into the future.

When did this first happen?

Next Thursday.

Most of us have experienced intuition, answered the phone knowing who's on the other end, or had that good gut feeling about a job, then got it.

"The only real valuable thing is intuition." Albert Einstein

Often we're reminded of the power of intuition only once we've ignored it. We look back and say, "if only I'd listened to myself", "if only I'd trusted my intuition", or "I knew something was wrong".

"Learn to let your intuition - gut instinct - tell you when the food, the relationship, the job isn't good for you (and conversely, when what you're doing is just right)."
Oprah Winfrey

Intuition, inner knowing, instinct, our sixth sense – though under-researched, it's a powerful part of us, perhaps the rationale for all our other senses.

Intuition is not about thinking. It's about knowing, that gut reaction, a strong sense about something that isn't based upon reason – we just know.

We all have the ability to be intuitive. Children are particularly good at it – they know when something's wrong or their parents are unhappy, no matter how hard they try to conceal it.

The more grounded and present we are, the more we can access our deep inner knowing.

"Trust your hunches... Hunches are usually based on facts filed away just below the conscious level."
Dr Joyce Brothers

"Sex is emotion in motion."
Mae West

Libido or sexual energy

Sigmund Freud coined the term "libido" to describe our sex drive, which he believed is driven by our id, the pleasure-seeking part of our psyche (see p.188).

So for him our libido is the part of us that controls our natural urges and our desire to take part in sexual activity.

Carl Jung widened this definition, arguing that the libido is also a powerful psychic energy responsible for creativity and our ability to strive as beings.

Our libido is affected by our state of mind (if we're depressed or anxious it can feel like our sex drive has driven off!). If we repress our natural desire for sexual activity, this too can affect how we think and feel – we're sexual beings after all.

The chemical most responsible for our sexual impulses is the hormone testosterone, present in both men and women.

Women's testosterone levels change as part of our menstrual cycle. More testosterone is released into the bloodstream a few days before we ovulate, and this increases our sex drive.

Some research suggests that the changing hormone levels generated by the contraceptive pill can also affect our libido.

If we feel depressed, stressed or tired we may become uninterested in sex.

Medication, including antidepressants, can also lower our libido.

If we are experiencing relationship difficulties with our sexual partner, this can often reduce our desire for sexual intimacy.

Life scripts

The term "life script" belongs to Transactional Analysis theory, a form of therapy that explores how we relate and why we say the things we do (see p.340).

Eric Berne and Claude Steiner were the first to define life scripts and to see that the scripts that we live are written in childhood and attached to a "payoff" or outcome. The scripts we learn become our life plan; they set up expectations and the assumptions we make about others, our life and who we are.

Our script is written during our first seven years of life, determined by what we learn from the people around us (and their life scripts!). It informs the way we see and make sense of the world, and the games we play and the behaviour we adopt to get by.

We take our script into adult life. Our script results in us forming the opinions we hold about what we deserve, whether we feel good enough or can fulfil our potential.

Ever noticed the patterns that keep occuring in your life? We may attract the same partner or situations at work – we may feel constantly bullied, rejected or down – we may never achieve, or get, what we want. Most of the time we might not be aware that the roles we assume are part of our script.

Our script sets us up to fail or succeed. It reinforces old patterns and beliefs, and the lines that were written while we were young have either helped or hindered us depending on what we want. But just as we learned our script, so we can unlearn it.

When we understand it, we can change our life script, unlearn old patterns and see things anew. We can choose new beliefs about ourselves and others, and use affirmations to reinforce these new things.

L

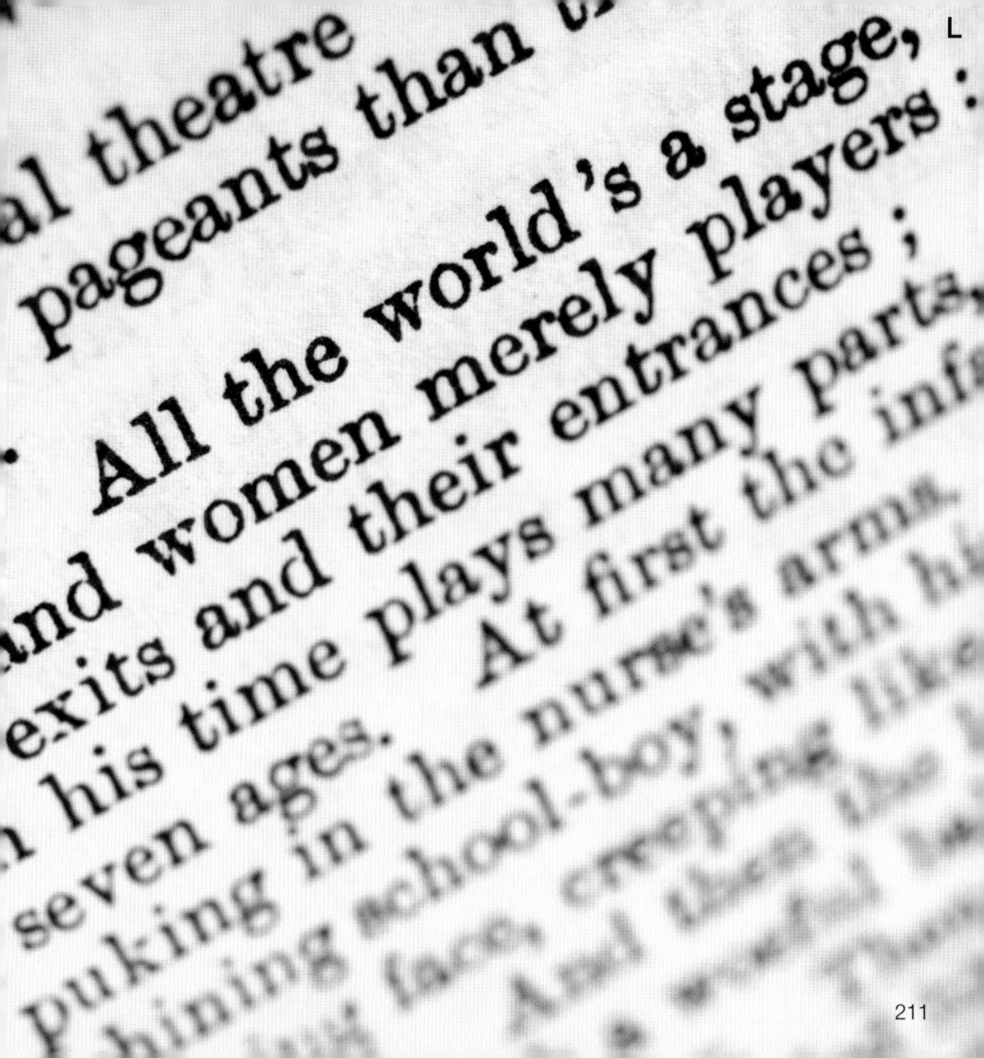

al theatre
pageants than t

All the world's a stage,
and women merely players:
exits and their entrances;
n his time plays many parts,
seven ages. At first the inf
puking in the nurse's arms.
hining school-boy, with hi
face, creeping like
And then the

Listening

"It's only through listening that you learn, I never want to stop learning."
Drew Barrymore

How often do we listen or feel listened to? Do we really feel heard as we share words with others?

Being listened to in an accepting and non-judgemental way is a powerful route to personal change. If someone is really listening, we feel safe to open up and we feel less defensive. We can share our true feelings and express ourselves clearly without censoring our words or experiences.

If we're listened to without criticism or judgement, our confidence and esteem can strengthen and grow, and we can express our true thoughts, ideas and feelings without being shot down, criticised or laughed at.

"If you judge people, you have no time to love them."
Mother Teresa

When we really listen, it helps others open up, our relationships can develop as we feel it's safe to open up and be intimate. Then our friends, family, partners and colleagues may feel they can share and be valued as we listen.

Listening is life a skill, an important quality for a counsellor or therapist; they're trained to listen and hear what we are saying (and not saying!). As we feel heard, we can soon hear ourselves, which can improve how we indeed hear others.

"I always talk to myself, it's the only way to ensure intelligent conversation."

Lithium

The word lithium comes from "lithos" – which is greek for stone (but we don't feel stoned if we take it).

Lithium medication helps stabilise our mood without acting as a sedative. If we need it long term, it helps balance mood swings, but also it can dampen imagination and our self-expression.

Lithium is a natural substance found in food and water. Small amounts can be found in our bodies naturally, but if we need lithium it's not because we're deficient in it.

Lithium is most commonly used to treat mania. Its effectiveness was discovered in 1949, by accident; it was tested on a group of patients and their symptoms improved.

It has been used since the second century. Soranus of Ephesus believed he could treat mania if people drank the water from the local spring – turns out the water had a high lithium content.

Like most medicinal drugs, lithium can be harmful if not taken correctly. It's important to talk to your doctor and follow their guidelines: lithium being a toxic metal, the dose that any of us takes needs to be precise.

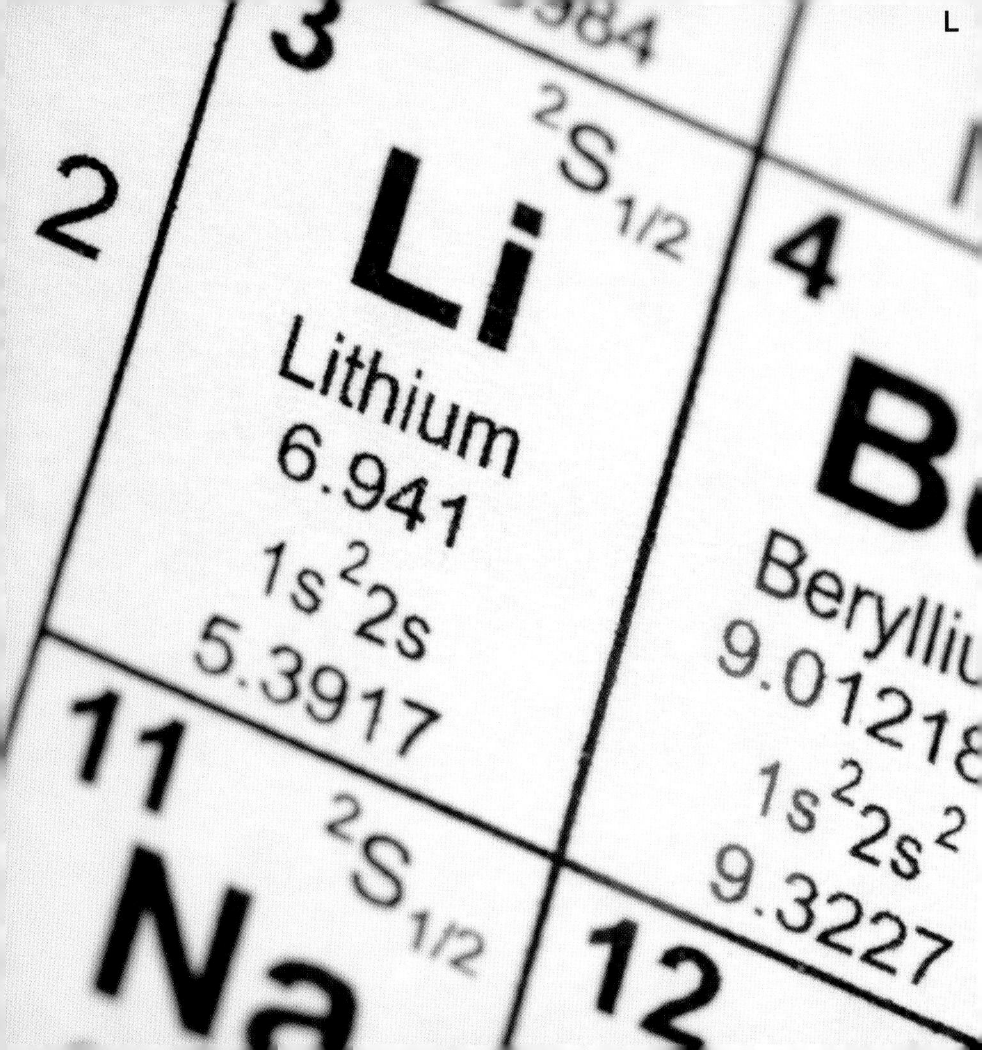

L
3
2
$^2S_{1/2}$
Li
Lithium
6.941
$1s^2 2s$
5.3917
4
9.01218
$1s^2 2s^2$
9.3227
11
$^2S_{1/2}$
Na
12

Love

We all need to love and be loved, loving and being loved is one of life's greatest joys.

"Love is always open arms. If you close your arms about love you will find that you are left holding only yourself."
Leo F. Buscaglia

What is love? … now there's a question!

Love can mean many things – affection, warmth, kindness, understanding, recognition, happiness …

Love is something we feel and do; we not only experience it, but we express it through our actions. Acts of kindness, forgiveness, compassion, understanding, humility, patience and acceptance are behavioural manifestations of love.

The Greeks have three words for love, agape, erotica and philia …

Agape is the broadest form of love. Unconditional, divine and thoughtful, it's a love that enables compassion and empathy.

Erotica is the love and affection we feel for our lovers; we feel and express it as we love with our bodies.

Philia is the love we feel for our family and social groups and for abstract concepts (e.g. philosophy = love of knowledge). It's a non-sexual love – affection towards our friends, family and co-workers.

For healthy, loving sexual relationships, we need a bit of all three, but unconditional love and non-sexual affection are what our mind needs most (especially if we're not in a relationship right now).

Most cultures and societies have attached powerful myths to the word 'love'.

L
“I have found the paradox, that if you love until it hurts, there can be no more hurt, only more love.” Mother Teresa

Love is most commonly associated with intimate sexual relationships, but the experience, feeling and quality of love can mean so much more than that.

Most of us are brought up believing that love is outside of us – it's something that arrives when we fall in love – but this is the myth that triggers heartbreak. Love is inside us, and it's there all the time; to feel it within, we just need to find it.

"True love doesn't come to us, it's within us."
Julia Roberts

Love is available to all of us, all the time. It's inside us, but sometimes gets hidden. Past pain or issues can get in the way of us feeling our own source of love within.

Our early experiences teach us about love, whether it's kind and caring and respectful, or about possession, power, neglect and abuse.

If the people we loved hurt or harmed us, we may look for a partner who treats us the same, because we think this is love and what we deserve or expect.

If the people we've loved abused or neglected us, it's hard to trust and love again – we may not feel lovable or feel love for ourselves.

"Love is a choice we make from moment to moment."
Barbara De Angelis

Feeling and giving our love to ourselves is the most important love we'll ever have.

When we feel the love we have for ourselves in our own hearts, we've a love forever that can soothe and protect us.

"The most important thing in life is to learn how to give out love, and to let it come in."
Morrie Schwartz

Some of us find it hard to love or even like who we are. This affects how we treat ourselves – our self-respect and self-regard, our sense of self-worth and our self-esteem, what we think we are worth and what we think we deserve.

How we feel about ourselves will affect the choices we make, the relationships we have and the way we let people treat us.

It's important to learn how to love, respect and look after ourselves; we can put ourselves first, without feeling guilty.

If we don't feel complete as we are, then we may allow relationships or work to fill up the gap.

We may look to another to feel happy or whole, and we may change who we are to keep their love … but when that love goes we're left with a even bigger hole.

With luck we may realise that this is a hole that only we can fill.

"You know it's love when all you want is that person to be happy, even if you're not part of their happiness." Julia Roberts

The love drug

"If you want to be loved, go out and love." Author unknown (bet they're lovely though!).

Though some of us might need medication (prescribed or otherwise) to enjoy our love life, the body actually supplies us with a love chemical. It's known as oxytocin.

Oxytocin is released in the brain when we experience affection between another and ourselves and when we touch someone or are sexually aroused.

Oxytoxin is the chemical hormone most associated with "falling in love".

Research has shown that people in happy, healthy loving relationships have higher levels of this hormone than others.

"Love is the best medicine, and there is more than enough to go around once you open your heart." Julie Marie

Oxytoxin is used in antidepressants and during the labour of childbirth.

"The flowering of love is meditation." Jiddu Krishnamurti

Affirmation: I am loved, loving and lovable, I love myself and others freely.

Meditation

Meditation is an ancient practice: it's been used for over 5,000 years as a way to calm and centre the mind and body. There are lots of ways to meditate, and although some practice is linked to religion we don't have to be religious to meditate.

When we meditate, we ask our mind to focus on one thing – it might be on our breath, on a candle flame or image, we might repeat a word or mantra over and over, we may focus on a part of our body … we can even slip a piece of chocolate into our mouth and meditate on the sensation and taste! We can learn to observe our thoughts and remain detached from them, like clouds as they drift across the sky.

At first, we may notice our thoughts jumping around, but with practice over a period of time – for some, weeks, for others, years – they settle and start to slow down.

The important thing is to realise that everyone's thoughts jump around, and there's nothing bad about it – we don't need to say "Oh blast, here I go again, how stupid I am!" but just be kind to ourselves and put the thought gently to one side – time after time, after time! Later on, we may realise that our mind is more present, and we feel more anchored and grounded within.

"Meditation is the soul's perspective glass."
Owen Feltham

As we slow down our mind, we slow down our body, which deepens our breathing, reduces our heart rate and calms our nervous system. Meditation promotes relaxation and provides rest for the body.

Most meditation techniques suggest sitting upright so the spine is straight, which helps breathing and energy flow. Our palms can face upwards as they rest in our lap, our eyes are closed unless we're focusing on something.

Meditation takes patience and practice.

By simply focusing our mind on our breath or our body, we will begin to notice out thoughts and detach from them.

The more we practise the easier it is, and the more we experience its benefits.

We can start by just sitting or lying quietly for 5 or 10 minutes each morning.

Memory

Doctor, Doctor I think I'm suffering from déjà vu!

Didn't I see you yesterday?

Our memory retains information, it's created by a series of activities in the brain: encoding or registration, storing and recording, retrieval and recall.

"Memory is the library of the mind."
Francis Fauvet-Gourand

A bit like a computer memory stick, our mind captures information, recognises/constructs it then stores it in a compartment for recall as we need it.

Why is a man different from a computer? You only have to ask a computer once!

There are three types of memory stores: sensory, short term and …oh I remember now! long-term memory.

Sensory memory captures information from our sensory system – sight, smell, touch, taste, hearing and "sixth sense" (like dowsing and intuition). Sensory memory holds information for a couple of seconds. Smell, more than any other sense, evokes memory.

Our short-term memory works for about 15–20 seconds – it helps us remember things like phone numbers before we dial them.

Long-term memory is a more permanent storage bank; here we store knowledge, things we have learned and memories of past experiences.

Some researchers believe that memory is 95% construct and 5% recall (depends how you see it, I'll have to remember that!).

"Memory is the diary we all carry with us." Oscar Wilde

Emotions are powerful triggers to memory – the memories easiest to recall are often attached to intense feelings, either happy or sad.

For most psychotherapists, our earliest memories are considered the most powerful; they tend to inform the way we live life as adults.

If we've painful old memories that we haven't grieved or worked through, old emotions may still be attached to them.

Psychotherapists are specially trained to explore past experiences and resolve our old hurts. It can be hard to look back and trawl through the past, but for some it's the key to unlocking the future.

"If you want to test your memory, try and remember what you were worrying about a year ago today!"
E. Joseph Cossman

Memory loss

Why are all blonde jokes one-liners? So men can remember them!

From time to time we all experience memory lapse, especially if we're ungrounded – we can't find our car keys, we forget people's names, where we've put something. This is perfectly normal (forgetting to pick the kids up is even more understandable!).

"A clear conscience is usually the sign of a bad memory." (author forgotten)

Though most people associate memory loss with old age, other factors can affect both our long- and short-term memory.

Stress and sleeping difficulties can affect our memory, as well as the menopause, depression and anxiety. Periods of being unconscious or head injuries are also associated with temporary or sometimes permanent memory loss.

Evidence suggests that electroconvulsive treatment (ECT) can also affect our memory function (if it doesn't erase it forever!) (see p,131).

Some people have extraordinary memories. Ben Pridmore of Boston in Lincolnshire was the 2004 World Memory Champion: he holds the world record for memorizing the random order of a pack of playing cards – just 26 seconds.

London taxi drivers are well known for their memories. Recent research has shown that the capital's cabbies' grey matter grows and adapts to help them store the streets of London in their heads!

Though we can't always rebuild or restore our memory, we can find ways of getting the best out of our mind, which can help:

1) Get plenty of fresh air, increasing oxygen supply to the brain helps it work better.
2) Eating a balanced diet with lots of fresh veg and fish: the brain needs nutrients just like the body.
3) Routine and healthy habits can reduce forgetfulness. Leave your keys, phone, (kids! even) in the same place each time you put them down.

4) Slow down, do one thing at a time, this helps the mind focus. Often when we've got too much going on we forget the important little things.
5) Talk to yourself, say a name a couple of times when you meet someone, say out loud where you've put something or what you're doing.
6) Use a diary or get a daily newspaper to help you remember what date it is. A diary can also help us remember things or our arrangements. (as long as we write them in there!)
7) Make up sayings or rhymes to remember things by.
8) Match images to people's faces or things we need to remember.
9) Avoid smoking or excessive drinking, this limits oxygen supply to the brain.
10) I've forgotten this one!
11) Take time to ground yourself, our memory works better if our mind is calm and present.

Mood

The term "mood" describes our affective state – how we feel. How often do we hear "I'm in a bad mood" or "I'm a good mood"?

Well, our mood is a less intense state than a feeling; it's a way of describing our general feeling most of the time. Like the climate (long-term) compared to the weather (which often changes daily).

But our mood can be short-lived or longer-term, depending on our state of mind.

Hormone levels can affect our mood, and women experiencing pre-menstrual tension or the menopause may experience mood changes to varying degrees. But most of the time these states don't last more than a few days.

Sometimes our mood will keep changing persistently, causing all kinds of difficulties for ourselves and others.

If we experience persistent mood changes we can talk to our doctor; we may need medication to balance things out, but perhaps it might be better to get to the source of these swings (see p.232).

Our mood is regulated by the chemicals in our brain and our thyroid, a butterfly-shaped gland that sits near the Adam's apple in our throat. Our thyroid produces hormones, which can affect our mood, our energy levels, weight gain and body temperature.

For some, mood can be very much affected by food.

"Bagels and doughnuts, round food for every mood."
Chandler from Friends

"On a bad day I have mood swings, on a good day I have the whole mood playground."
Charles Rosenblum

M

Mood stabilisers

Mood stabilisers are a type of drug that can help us if we are experiencing difficulties with our mood. There are a number of mood stabilisers, including lithium, carbamazepine and sodium valproate.

It's not known how the medication actually works but they're non-addictive drugs that are believed to even out the speed at which the brain operates and how quickly it passes information throughout the nervous system; they may also correct chemical imbalances in the brain. Drugs used as mood stabilisers include lithium, widely used to treat mania.

Valproate semisodium (Depakote) is also used for the treatment of mania. Its effects are calming, it slows down the sending of brain messages to a normal rate. Approximately 50% of people having a manic episode respond to valproate. The effects of valproate are often felt soon after taking it.

Carbamazepine is used mainly in the treatment of mood disorders. In order to be effective, carbamazepine has to reach a given level in the blood. In order to monitor this and to investigate whether we're on the best dosage, we may need to have several blood tests while we adjust to the drug. It may take several months for it to achieve the best results.

Lamotrigine is particularly effective for people with the depressive symptoms of manic depression. Lamotrigine should begin to work as soon as you start taking the tablets. It is a preventative medicine that will probably need to be taken for a long time – months, or even years.

Atypical antipsychotics. The newer antipsychotics have been found to have mood stabiliser properties and are now licensed for the treatment of manic depression. The first drugs of this class to be licensed were olanzapine and quetiapine.

Mood swings

If we experience persistent changes in mood that seem inappropriate, distorted or out of context, we may be experiencing mood swings, otherwise known as cyclothmia.

Cyclothmia is a form of bipolar disorder, but is less extreme; it involves short periods of mild depression and short periods of what's known as hypomania, elation or irritability. In between each phase we also experience normal mood levels.

Cyclothmia is most common amongst those approaching adulthood – a challenging time for any of us. Life-changing decisions have to be made as we leave home and begin to discover who we are. It's often experienced if we're extremely intelligent or creative.

Unresolved childhood trauma can also lead to our experiencing cyclothmia.

Cyclothmia can be treated. Talking to a therapist can help, and sometimes medication is used to treat extreme symptoms of the condition as with depression or mania.

A psychiatrist can diagnose cyclothmia, they can help us put together a treatment plan, it's perfectly possible to live a normal and happy life if we experience the condition.

M

“In my experience, there is only one motivation, and that is desire. No reasons or principle contain it or stand against it.”

Jane Smiley

Motivation

"I once went into a bookstore and asked the saleswoman, 'Where's the self-help section?' She said if she told me, it would defeat the purpose." George Carlin

If you've read this far, it's because you've been motivated to … what drives and motivates us may be conscious or unconscious. Our motives for behaving the way we do tell us a lot about ourselves, but sometimes our motives are outside our awareness.

Motive, though normally associated with crime, is what drives us to do everything we do; motive can be self-advancing or self-deprecating, depending on the outcome.

Motivation takes us places; if we believe we can do or have something, motivation gets us there.

If we're motivated to do something it's very likely we will, because motivation gives us energy and get up and go, and supports us when the going gets tough …

"Every mistake may turn out to be the one thing necessary to a worthwhile achievement." Henry Ford

Our motivation levels can be affected by our mood and how we are feeling, and if our motivation is low we may be experiencing resistance or procrastination.

If we've been feeling depressed or anxious, though we may want to make plans and set goals, we find it hard to do that and work towards achieving them.

So if we can work through our anxiety and depression, we can soon set to on our goals.

Multiple Personality Disorder (MPD)

MPD is also known as Dissociative Identity Disorder (DID). It's the most complex of the dissociative disorders (see p.122).

If we experience DID, we display several identities that reveal themselves like different personalities, each identity controlling our behaviour or thoughts at any one time. Each identity has a different way of thinking and relating to the world. One identity may have no idea when the other identity is in control, or even that there is another identity.

What causes dissociative disorders is open to debate. Some experts believe that they can be directly linked to trauma or abuse, while others argue they are a result of disruptions to the normal parent/child relationship or a disturbance during childhood development.

Studies have shown that a history of trauma is almost universal for people who experience extreme dissociative symptoms; usually this is a result of abuse in childhood.

"The commercial sexual exploitation and abuse of children is nothing less than a form of terrorism – one whose wanton destruction of young lives and futures must not be tolerated for another year, another day, another hour."
Carol Bellamy

M

Music therapy

Music therapy is helpful in several ways; it's a means of communication and self-expression, it relaxes us and it allows us to ground ourselves as our senses get lost in sound. It can bring us unalloyed joy to play an instrument, sing or write our own music.

If we choose to explore music therapy, it's music making, rather than words, that becomes the main form of communication. We don't need to be a musician or play an instrument to take part in music therapy – just enthusiasm and interest. Very often, percussion instruments such as drums, chime bars or bells can be used to create meaningful sounds.

Music therapy can take place on a one-to-one basis or as part of a group.

If we take part in music therapy we're encouraged to explore our own voice as well as the different kinds of sounds other instruments can make to convey sound and meaning, and evoke feelings and emotions.

"Music expresses feeling and thought, without language; it was below and before speech, and it is above and beyond all words."
Robert G. Ingersoll

Music therapy can help increase our self-awareness, help us explore emotions and feelings. We may end up writing songs and, by creating a piece of music, be able to heal or come to terms with old wounds or painful memories.

"Music is your own experience, your thoughts, your wisdom. If you don't live it (or blow it even) it won't come out of your horn." Charlie Parker

Nervous breakdown

"Sometimes a breakdown can be the beginning of a kind of breakthrough, a way of living in advance through a trauma that prepares you for a future of radical transformation."
Cherrie Moraga

A "nervous breakdown" is a non-medical catchall term used to describe a sudden and acute episode of mental dis-ease. It's not a clinical term.

If we're having a breakdown, chances are we're finding it hard to cope, we can't think straight, we might see, hear things or imagine things, appear paranoid or manic and be unable to manage (and we're certainly not feeling grounded!).

We might be feeling extremely agitated, unable to sleep, relax, concentrate or attend to things; we might be feeling frightened or anxious, angry or extremely sad. We might have to go to hospital to get some medical help with the symptoms of a breakdown, or just to get some time out.

Many things can trigger a nervous breakdown: bereavement, career burnout, bullying, an identity crisis or a traumatic event.

Breakdowns can be breakthroughs (if you let them be). At times in our lives we might need to break down, in order to build life back up. We might need to explore what's led to this experience, what can we learn, what needs to change.

"From time to time, life as a leader can look hopeless. To help you, consider a man who lived through this:

Failed in business at age 31.
Defeated for the legislature at 32.
Again failed in business at 34.
Sweetheart died at 35.
Had a nervous breakdown at 36.
Defeated in election at 38.
Defeated for Congress at 43.
Defeated for Congress at 46.
Defeated for Congress at 48.
Defeated for Senate at 55.
Defeated for Vice President at 56.
Defeated for Senate at 58.
Elected President at age 60...
This man was Abraham Lincoln".
Anon

Neurosis

"Education, like neurosis, begins at home."
Milton R. Sapirstein

Dr William Cullen first used "neurosis" in 1769 as a mental health term, to describe illnesses associated with the nervous system, conditions that could not be explained in physical terms.

During the eighteenth and nineteenth centuries, the term "neurosis" described a number of nervous disorders and symptoms that have since been singled out and relabelled in the DSM IV (see p.129).

The term very much belonged to the psychoanalytic school of therapists – guys like Freud and Jung – but today it's a loose definition that could be applied to a number of conditions from anxiety to personality disorder.

In fact, the term is so redundant today, it's been removed from the DSM IV. It has many stigmas attached to it and is often misused.

The word "neurosis" originates from the Greek words "neuron" meaning nerve and "osis" meaning disease.

"The scars left from the child's defeat in the fight against irrational authority are to be found at the bottom of every neurosis."
Erich Fromm

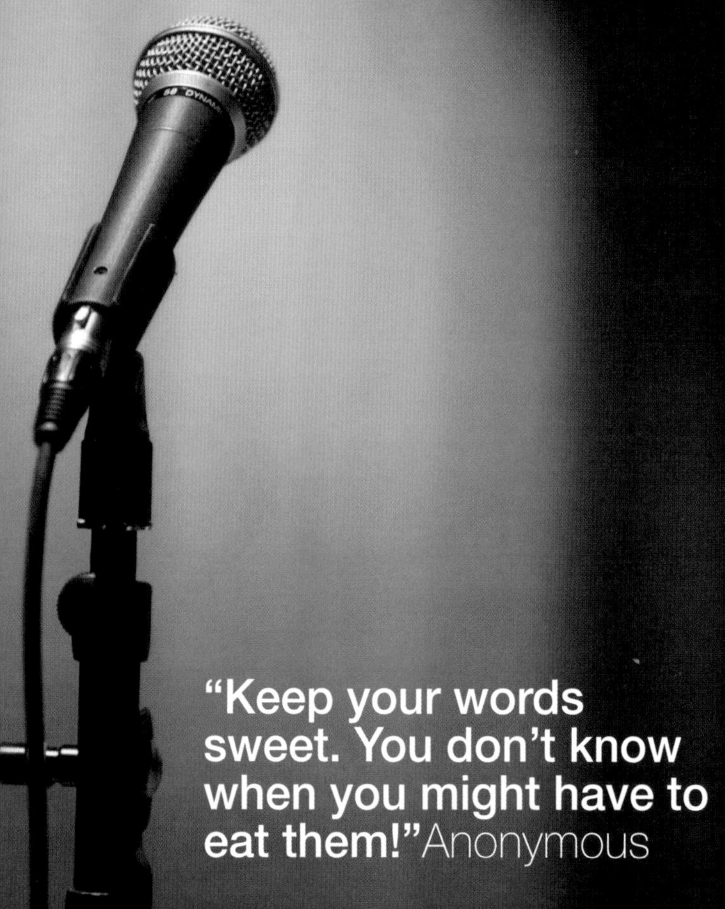

"Keep your words sweet. You don't know when you might have to eat them!" Anonymous

NLP

NLP stands for Neuro-linguistic Programming: it's a type of talking therapy and theory.

"NLP is about a connection with thoughts, speech and action and how we connect with others, the world and our spirituality." Joseph O'Connor and Ian McDermott

The premise of NLP comes from the idea that if one person can do something, so can someone else – so NLP seeks to explore what gets in the way.

"Neuro" refers to our mind and how we organise our life in terms of thinking: if we think we can do something then we probably will.

"Linguistic" is about language – how we use it and how it affects us. NLP can help us learn to take responsibility for how we communicate and to understand how others respond – and also that the way we say things can influence the response we get.

"Programming" is – in this sense! – about our repetitive behaviour and how we act with purpose. NLP can help us explore our repetitive patterns and break out of them.

Richard Bandler and John Grinder developed NLP in the 1970s as an interpersonal communication model. It was created as an alternative to psychotherapy.

NLP can provide us with techniques and strategies to improve our communication and help bring about the changes we want to see in our lives.

Noradrenaline/norepinephrine

Noradrenaline is a substance released naturally by our body's nerve cells. It has a number of effects, but when our body produces it, it's the chemical responsible for the way we freeze in stressful situations.

As noradrenaline is released, our heart rate quickens, our blood pressure increases, our pupils and airways dilate and the blood vessels in our non-essential organs narrow. This is what prepares us to perform as well as we can in stressful situations.

Noradrenaline can be used to restore blood pressure to normal in emergency situations when blood pressure has dropped dangerously low.

"Women are more social in the way they cope with stress. Men are more likely to deal with stress with a fight or flight reaction. Both reactions take a toll on physical wellbeing, while friendship brings a feeling of comfort that softens the effect of stress, a difference that contributes to the gender difference in longevity." Shelley Taylor

N

When you don't know where to turn, turn inwards!

Obsessive compulsive disorder (OCD)

If we experience OCD, we feel as though we've no control of certain thoughts, ideas, or urges. These things appear to force themselves into our mind, and as they're often distressing and unacceptable to us, this makes it hard to share our experience with others.

Within the obsession we are experiencing, we have an underlying belief that either we or others will come to some harm. Because we can't dismiss this belief it creates anxiety and we may feel helpless – all we feel we can do is perform a ritual which helps rid us of the devastating thought. OCD is driven by irrational fear.

The rituals we perform are known as compulsions; repeatedly opening or closing a door, hand washing, repeating words or sentences. We do these things over and over again because we fear we didn't do them properly the first time!

We fear the frightening thoughts may come back, so our relief from anxiety is only short-lived.

OCD is similar to a phobia (see p.274). All humans double-check things from time to time, but with OCD the problems are so extreme they interfere with everyday life. We may spend eight hours of our day ritualising or compulsing rather than getting on with other things.

There are several theories as to why we may develop OCD. Some believe it's lack of serotonin, others believe it's a result of personal or childhood experiences. OCD is linked to trauma and being sexually abused.

Some believe the perfectionists amongst us are more prone to developing the condition, but that whatever causes it can be overcome. Many organisations and counsellors can help us manage and overcome obsessive compulsions.

Mind state some 3% of the UK population experience some form of OCD.

Over-adaptation

"Adapt or perish, now as ever, is nature's inexorable imperative." H. G. Wells

Many of us experience over-adaptation. We over-adapt when we put others first, and discount our own needs but respond to the needs – or our imagined needs – of others.

"We talk of our mastery of nature, which sounds very grand; but the fact is we respectfully adapt ourselves, first, to her ways"
Clarence Day

Over-adaptation is a survival mechanism. It's often learned in childhood. If our basic needs for recognition, love and acceptance aren't met, we adapt who we are in order to cope.

We may attempt to please others to seek praise or reward, or we may behave badly to get swift and certain attention. For most of us, unpleasant attention is better than none at all.

Being adaptable is helpful – it enables us to be flexible in a situation, and it helps us negotiate and explore opportunities.

But … if we're always over-adaptive we're not being real, and we may need to play games to get our needs met, which is not so healthy.

As we learn to understand why we over-adapt, we can quickly learn new ways of behaving. It's important to put ourselves first. As we become more self-supporting, we can ask for what we want, or meet our needs within.

Chinese proverb say…"the wise adapt themselves to circumstances; water moulds itself to a pitcher."

Overeating

"Eating rice cakes is like chewing on a foam coffee cup, only less filling."
Dave Barry

BED, or binge eating, has only recently been recognised as a disorder in its own right; it was registered as a disorder in 1992. We use overeating as an attempt to heal.

People with BED binge uncontrollably, but don't purge themselves in the same way as people do with bulimia nervosa (see p.88). So, because of the large amounts of food they eat, people with BED can become obese, which leads to other health problems.

Signs of binge eating are when we eat more quickly than usual, we feel uncomfortable eating around others, we eat until we are uncomfortably full or we may feel out of control around food.

We often feel guilty about eating the amount we do.

We can overcome eating disorders; if we can understand what's causing our need to overeat, we can soon improve our eating habits.

There are a number of organisations that deal specifically with eating disorders. They are listed at the back of the book.

"Eating words has never given me indigestion."
Winston Churchill

Compulsive overeating

With compulsive overeating, we tend to eat when we're not hungry. This can happen all the time or can come and go. We use our food in the hope that it can be a way to heal, eating to comfort ourselves rather than satisfy our appetite.

If we're a compulsive eater, we tend to be overweight. We use our weight to hide our experience, and sufferers can experience shame about being unable to control the compulsion to eat.

"Food is the most basic forum for discussing things like love and the absence of love; how we hurt ourselves and how we heal ourselves."
Laura Benanti

All compulsive eating disorders can seriously affect our health, but there's help available through many organisations.

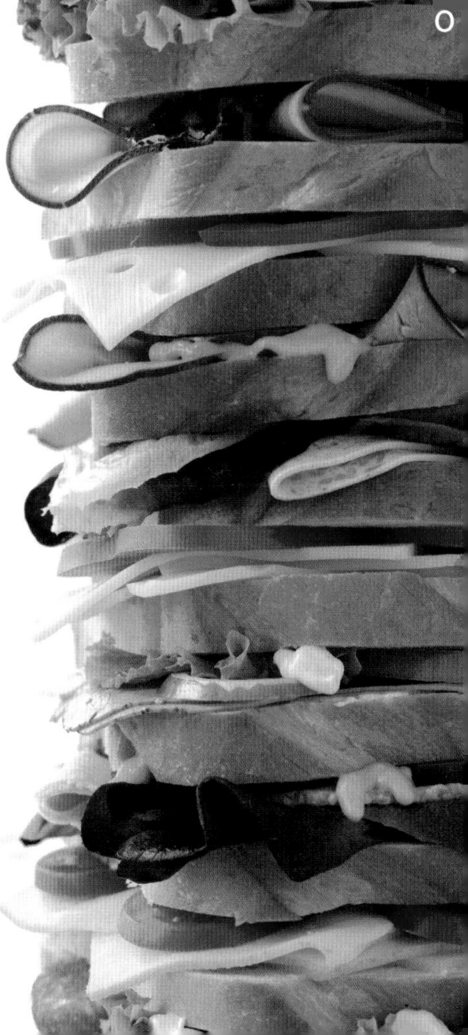

Panic attacks

One in every 75 people worldwide will experience a panic attack; it's one of the most common anxiety disorders. Why we experience panic can range from problems with our diet to stress or emotional issues.

Panic attacks are terrifying; they appear out of nowhere. We feel out of control, unable to breathe – our heart beats so hard we think it's exploding, we feel like we're mad or are about to die.

"Panic is a sudden desertion of us, and a going over to the enemy of our imagination."
Christian Nevell Bovee

With panic attacks, we may experience feelings of unreality, known as depersonalisation and derealisation. With depersonalisation, we feel detached from our body and surroundings, and with derealisation we feel grounded inside but the world seems far away.

When we have a panic attack it's an exaggerated experience of our body's normal response to fear, stress or excitement. As we face a situation that could be dangerous, our body gears up by producing adrenaline – but, though our flight or fight response was useful when we lived in caves it's not always appropriate to life today.

Panic attacks can last from 20 seconds to 5 minutes, we may have one or two together, some people have them several times a week, and they can even start in our sleep!

Panic attacks seem unpredictable and therefore uncontrollable, but this is not always the case. If we've experienced lots of panic attacks, we may develop a fear of fear, living in constant worry of another attack. We may avoid places and social situations, and at worst become agoraphobic, which can really affect our quality of life. Multiple and prolonged panic attacks can lead to depression.

There's a number of reasons why we get a panic attack; it may be associated with a particular event or situation – flying or going to the dentist – or it be could be because of our childhood experiences, a repressed trauma. Survivors of abuse can experience panic attacks, and if we experience anxiety we can be prone to them too.

Then there are physiological factors; a sudden drop in our blood sugar level, drug withdrawal, over-breathing, antidepressants, asthma, or taking cocaine or marijuana – all these can induce a panic attack.

"We experience moments absolutely free from worry. These brief respites are called panic!" Cullen Hightower

Though it might not feel possible from our past experience, with time and commitment we can learn to control them. We can start by exploring whether they are linked to anything – any particular times, events, thoughts, smells, sights, foods …

We can learn to use creative visualisation, we can train our thoughts to follow a more positive direction and we can create relaxing images in our minds that we can recall; any of these will help if we feel we're about to panic (Brad Pitt comes to mind).

We can use affirmations and talk to ourselves positively, calmly and firmly to help ground us. We can learn to be assertive: it may be that stress in our job, relationship, family is resulting in us feeling overwhelmed or anxious, or losing confidence in ourselves.

We can take relaxation classes and learn to breathe properly, which can help keep us calm. Eating regularly and properly – avoiding "sugar hits" – can help too; avoiding stimulants can also lower our propensity to panic.

Medication is available to treat some forms of panic attacks, and the talking therapies can help us identify what triggers attacks and explore any deeper issues that may be contributing to them.

Paranoia

Most of us have experienced paranoia to some degree or other; sometimes we feel a bit suspicious about people's motives, or that people are up to something behind our backs. But sometimes what may seem like paranoia is actually intuition, so it helps to check it out – what evidence can we find for our feeling?

If we're paranoid all the time, we live in dread of a forthcoming betrayal or attack by other people. We think something awful is going to happen or try to second-guess what adversaries might do, in order to outwit them. Fears become focused on the future rather than rationally worked through or reality-tested. In extreme forms of paranoia, reality cannot be distinguished from fantasy – but of course if we're the paranoid person we can't possibly realise that!

Paranoia is a debilitating condition. We feel as though we can't trust, depend or rely upon anyone, including our nearest and dearest. Then the problem turns into a self-fulfilling prophecy, because our lack of trust in them results in them getting fed up and behaving negatively towards us, so we can see we can't trust them … We can become angry, vengeful or guilt-ridden, and we may isolate ourselves and end up depressed as a result. Extreme forms of the condition include paranoid schizophrenia, paranoid personality disorder and delusional or paranoid disorder.

There are many, many factors that can contribute to paranoia. It's a symptom of some 80 different mental health conditions. It has roots in our past but is also something we can experience alongside Parkinson's and Alzheimer's disease or can be experienced as part of old age.

Paranoia can be experienced as a thinking error. If we were taught that the world (especially our home) is an unsafe place, or that

Affirmation: I can learn to trust my world and others.

people are untrustworthy, this will increase the likelihood of our becoming paranoid. Paranoia can be a reaction to stressful life events – and don't forget, some delusions can turn out to be true.

Excessive drug use – and for some people this is a very small amount indeed, maybe just their first experiment – can affect our sense of reality; people have often experienced paranoia when using drugs, especially marijuana. If we think we're affected, a GP is the first point of call; they can put us in touch with a psychiatrist or clinical psychologist who can diagnose and help treat the condition (but only if we trust them!).

Antipsychotic and neuroleptic medication can also be used to treat paranoia, and some find community support groups and the talking therapies helpful.

Talking to a counsellor or therapist can help us share our experiences without being judged. We can learn how to trust, and to explore our thought processes, and we can learn how to test our seemingly paranoid thoughts to check if they're valid.

It's challenging for any of us to live with someone who has the condition. It's important to be positive with them, support good judgement, be as honest as we can, minimise the inevitable confrontations, and try to foresee and defuse problems that might lie ahead. And to keep our cool when we're constantly blamed for everything!

If we know someone with paranoia it's important to establish facts from assumption. It's also important to encourage independence in someone with paranoia; help is available as long as the person isn't too paranoid to accept it.

But there is the terrible irony that if we experience paranoia, we can become so deluded that we believe there's nothing wrong with us, so that if someone is trying to persuade us to go to the GP for a diagnosis, we believe they're doing something underhand, and that they're hostile to us.

Passive aggression

Passive aggression is about meeting our needs in an inappropriate way … rather than saying "I don't want to do the dishes" we drop a plate.

"Action, to be effective, must be directed to clearly conceived ends." Jawaharlal Nehru

Most of us behave this way from time to time, but if we do it a lot it affects our relationships and the people we love.

By being passive aggressive, we manipulatively, rather than openly or assertively, get our unconscious or conscious needs met.

What's more, passive aggression is a form of behaviour that avoids intimacy and so it can destroy the hope of any healthy – rather than manipulative – relationship.

"The actions of men are the best interpreters of their thoughts." John Locke

Affirmation: I can meet my needs directly (or dreckly if you're Cornish!)

Passive aggression is about meeting our needs in an inappropriate way – we drop a plate rather than saying "I don't want to do the dishes!"

Passivity

"To make oneself an object, to make oneself passive, is a very different thing from being a passive object."
Simone de Beauvoir

Passivity is a Transactional Analysis term developed by Schiff et al. (1971) that describes 4 types of unassertiveness.

If we behave in a passive way, we respond to problems in a way that puts us at a disadvantage, and our actions – or lack of them – get in the way of solving problems or moving on. If we behave passively, we're waving a flag that attracts aggressive people to us.

Passive behaviour can be linked to fear of hurting others, needing to please others or keeping others happy at our own expense. As a passive person, we may find it hard to participate in life fully.

The four kinds of passivity are...

- **Doing nothing -** We do nothing, we discount and fail to acknowledge the resources and power we have that will enable us to deal with a situation.
- **Incapacitation -** We experience incapacitation, the energy we have to solve a problem either turns inwards onto ourselves or outwards against other people, sometimes violently.
- **Over-adaptation -** We put our energy and effort into meeting the imagined or unchecked-out needs of others; we put others' needs before our own, and because we believe the ability of others to ask for what they want or need is similar to our own – i.e. non-existent – we deny them the opportunity of acting assertively.
- **Agitation -** We behave in an agitated way, we operate without a purpose. It's a way of releasing the tension that's arisen because we've not acted in a way to get our needs met.

Most of us experience a level of passivity at some point or other, but if we behave in this way a lot of the time, our lives and relationships can suffer. We end up feeling cheated, defeated and unfulfilled.

Assertion training or talking therapies can help us work through why we've developed this behaviour; we can learn new skills and value ourselves so that we can go out into the world and get what we want.

"Take time to deliberate; but when the time for action arrives, stop thinking and go in." Napoleon Bonaparte

Patience

Rome wasn't built in a day! Patience is something we have to learn (I can't wait to master it!).

Any parent will know we're certainly not born with it, but it's a useful quality for a healthy mind.

Patience comes with a peaceful mind. When we're patient, we're confident that we'll get there and so we can allow the process to take its own time.

When we're patient we don't need to force circumstances, we can go with the flow feeling confident and safe and at ease with the world.

"All human wisdom is summed up in two words – wait and hope."
Alexandre Dumas Père

When we are patient with ourselves, we can be patient with others (and that really is a virtue).

Patience helps us live in the present moment – we can understand this by knowing that if we're continually wanting things now, we exist in the future.

Patience comes to us as we feel more content.

"The marvel of all history is the patience with which men and women submit to burdens unnecessarily laid upon them by their governments." Author unknown

Affirmation: I trust that life will give me what I need, as and when I need it. Everything is as it should be.

"The key to everything is patience.
You get the chicken by hatching
the egg, not by smashing it."
Arnold H. Glasgow

Patterns = same shit - different day!

Life has a funny way of teaching us. Ever noticed the same things happening over and over again? We find we've picked the same kind of partner when it all goes tits up, we repeatedly fail but never know why … without meaning to, we end up making the same mistakes: "Why does this always happen to me?"

If we've unresolved issues in the back of our mind, we unconsciously play out old patterns and behaviours in order to heal or release the energy, but unfortunately rather than getting what we want, it gets in the way.

We repeatedly set ourselves up for rejection: we've had a number of abusive partners, we always end up the underdog, or we never get that promotion.

The patterns we experience are formed by our mind but as we explore them we can change what we do – we won't be drawn to the same situations, we'll seek different partners or we feel set to succeed.

"As long as habit and routine dictate the pattern of living, new dimensions of the soul will not emerge."
Henry Van Dyke

Breaking out of old patterns is hard to do alone – but a therapist can help us explore what might be leading us into repetitive patterns.

Once we understand what's unconsciously motivating these decisions or behaviour, we can break out of habits and set ourselves free.

"Continuing to cling to the patterns you know inhibits your ability to discover what you don't know." Eric Allenbaugh

Peace of mind

"Do not confuse peace of mind with spaced-out insensitivity. A truly peaceful mind is very sensitive, very aware." Dalai Lama

Peace of mind is a mind free from worry, anxiety and dis-ease. With peace of mind we feel a deep sense of inner calm and confidence, and we feel safe and at ease in the world around us – quiet, content and confident.

"Success is peace of mind which is a direct result of self-satisfaction in knowing you did your best to become the best you are capable of becoming." John Wooden

Developing a peaceful mind can take time. We might need to understand ourselves a bit better, and perhaps learn kind and positive affirmations to clear our heads of negative messages.

We might want to try yoga, meditation, breathing or relaxation exercises to bring ourselves back into our bodies and inner stillness.

Taking time to be quiet and still can also help us develop a sense of inner peace. Developing self-awareness and learning how to exist in the present moment can help too.

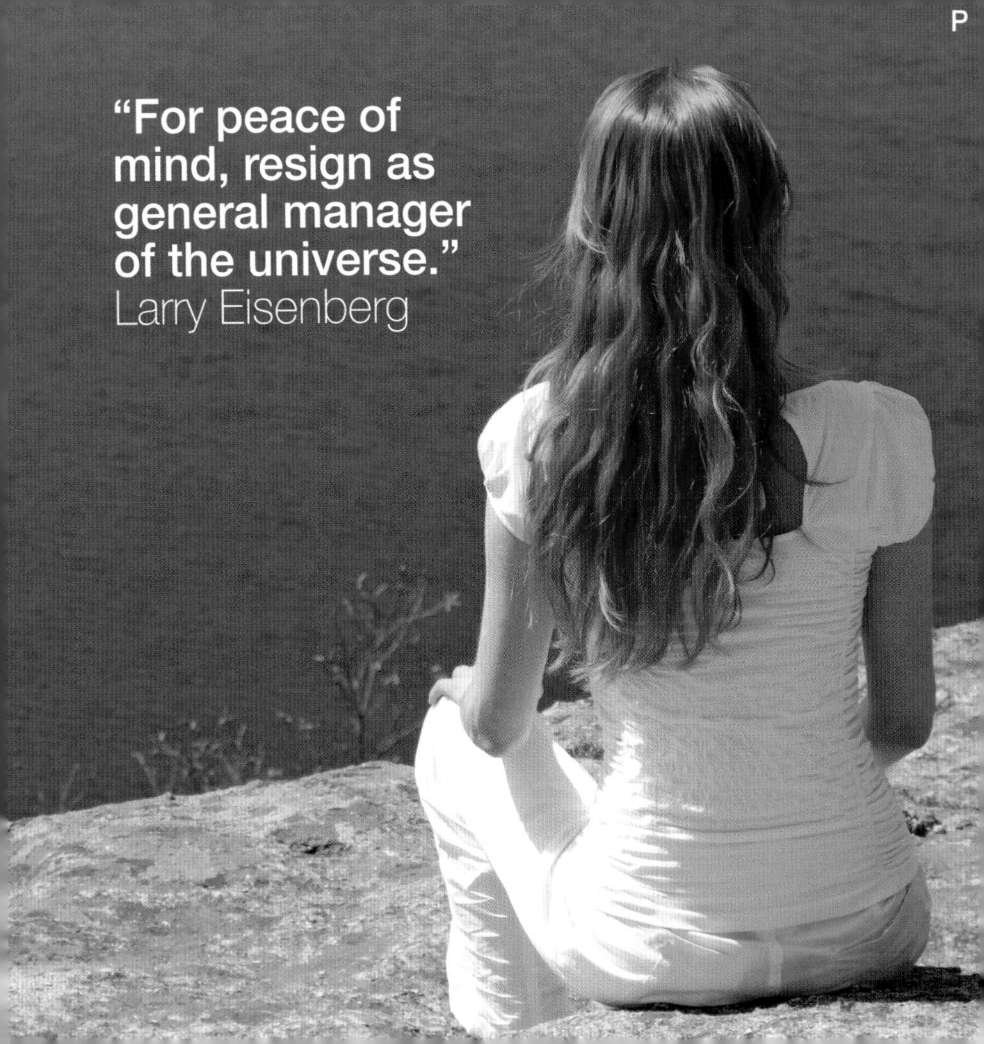
P
"For peace of mind, resign as general manager of the universe."
Larry Eisenberg

Perception

Our perception is about what we see or what we think we see, how we view the world, how we take sensory information on board, and what we do with it. What one person takes from an experience will be different from what another takes; we all look at the world through different spectacles (and some are rose tinted, some are not).

"The reality of life is that your perceptions – right or wrong – influence everything else you do. When you get a proper perspective on your perceptions, you may be surprised how many other things fall into place."
Roger Birkman

We learn how to see the world in a particular way. Our experiences as children will show us whether people are supportive or trustworthy, whether it's safe to share our experiences, whether work is unfulfilling or enjoyable, and whether life is fun or a great big slog for little, if any, reward.

The way we absorb experiences while we're small may not be much use to us as we grow into adults. Our perceptions filter our experiences, so that what we perceive is often different from what other people see, and either or neither may not be as whatever it is really is, and we need to realise, too, that what we fail to see is just as important as what we see.

Our perception affects how we relate to the world and how we relate to others. If we believe people are untrustworthy then this is what we'll see, whether it's real or not.

Affirmation:
I can learn to see things in different ways.

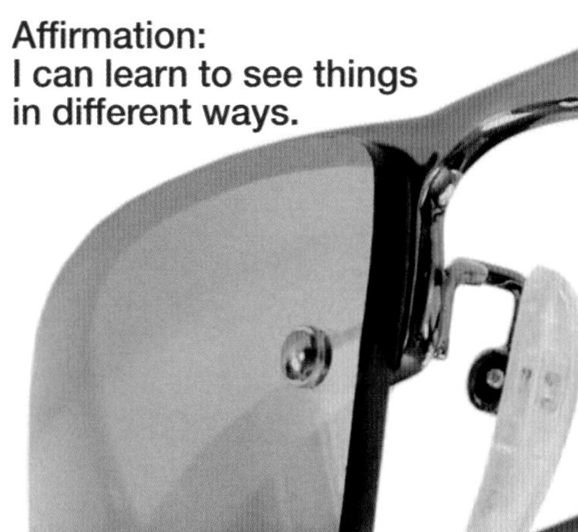

We come to situations with a particular way of seeing, and if we change how we see things, then life can look very different.

"Miracles happen every day, change your perception of what a miracle is and you'll see them all around you." Jon Bon Jovi

Changing our perception of things involves learning how to check things out and to test our reality and the assumptions we make about people and events. Some things are not always quite what they seem!

Permission

"Poor is the man whose pleasures depend on the permission of another."
Madonna

We spend most of our childhood being told what we can and can't do, what we can and can't have, how we should or shouldn't feel, what we should or shouldn't say, what we should and shouldn't do.

These messages based on "should" and "must" get laid down deep in the back of our minds; they often replay themselves later and when they do they restrict our choices.

We may want things but not allow ourselves to have them; we may want to try something but don't give ourselves a chance; some of us may want to speak our minds but don't think it's okay to do that.

"If it's a good idea, go ahead and do it. It's much easier to apologize than it is to get permission."
Grace Murray Hopper

If we don't feel worthy we won't reward ourselves; we restrain ourselves from having things or from enjoying new experiences. We end up feeling dissatisfied with life or unhappy that we're not reaching our full potential.

"When you take charge of your life, there is no longer a need to ask permission of other people or society at large. When you ask permission, you give someone veto power over your life." Albert F. Geoffrey

When we give ourselves permission we get back in charge; permission is food for our mind. Giving ourselves permission to have, learn and change can make all the difference. We all have the capacity to follow our hearts.

"We need to give ourselves permission to act out our dreams and visions, not look for more sensations, more phenomena, but live our strongest dreams even if it takes a lifetime."
Vijali Hamilton

Person-centred counselling

Carl Rogers (1902–1987) was the founder of person-centred counselling.

He believed that as individuals we are the best authority on our own experience, and that if we want to, each of us is capable of taking charge of our life and fulfilling our potential.

In order to "self actualize", Rogers felt we need to experience certain conditions.

Just as a seed needs sunshine, soil and water to grow and flourish, so humans need to experience empathy, congruence and unconditional positive regard. These "core" conditions are at the heart of person-centred counselling.

Person-centred counselling offers us the opportunity to explore where we're at, what we want to go to, and how we might get there.

Person-centred counselling is one of the humanist therapies, alongside Gestalt and existential therapy.

Humanist therapies recognise and respect that each and every one of us has the capacity and resources to work through our problems.

Person-centred counselling doesn't focus on the past; it's about understanding our present situation and what's available within us if we want to change it.

Just as a seed needs sunshine, soil and water to grow and flourish, humans need to experience empathy, congruence and unconditional positive regard.

Phobias

Phobophobia – the fear of having a phobia!

A phobia is an intense and irrational fear. We develop phobias around situations or objects that wouldn't normally worry others (unless they had the same phobia as us, that is!). If we experience phobia, it can affect us in different ways – some phobias are manageable but in extreme cases they affect our quality of life.

1 in 10 women have a fear of spiders or arachnophobia.

Phobia is an anxiety disorder – it's a bit like OCD or panic attacks in that phobia centres around our natural reaction and propensity to feel fear.

Acrophobia is fear of heights.

As children, we're taught or learn for ourselves what's dangerous and should be avoided: fire, dogs, ladders or water. A healthy level of fear keeps us safe from harm.

Fear of flying is known as aerophobia, it's one of the most common phobias.

It's normal to be wary about going high up out of our normal environment in something that looks like a big cigar case, but it's unreasonable – not to say often highly inconvenient! – to allow our fears to overwhelm our rational knowledge that flying is (statistically at least!) a lot safer than crossing the street.

With phobia, our sense of fear develops in response to things or objects that aren't necessarily that threatening. The fear we feel is out of all proportion to the thing that creates it.

Emetophobia is the fear of being sick or seeing others vomit.

Phobia can develop as a response to experiencing long-term stress and anxiety, and unhappy relationships. Problems about money or poor living conditions can increase our vulnerability to developing phobia.

Mysophobia is the term to describe the fear of germs or dirt.

Claustrophobia is fear of small spaces, agoraphobia is fear of open spaces (some people fear both!).

If we have a phobia, it can be a terrifying experience. If we are confronted by the thing we are phobic of we can become overwhelmed with terror – it can feel like we're facing an inevitable disaster, and we feel we need to escape.

Ophidiophobia describes the fear of snakes.

With phobia, we believe in the extreme responses we create in response to the triggers. We really do think we're facing a disaster, and we fear it will happen again. In extreme cases we avoid going out … we stay at home because it's where we're safest.

Cynophobia is the fear of dogs.

Phobias can be overcome; we can develop new coping strategies and ways of managing extreme emotions. We can learn new thought processes or techniques to help us deal with panic or anxiety.

Astraphobia is the fear of thunder and lightening.

Though medication doesn't cure phobia, short-term medical treatment can help ease some of the symptoms. Some people find hypnotherapy helpful, and some talk things through with a counsellor or therapist. We can also talk to our doctor.

Trypanophobia is the fear of having injections.

Physical abuse

We experience physical abuse when someone intentionally hurts or injures us. They may hit, kick, shake or beat us; they may throw objects at us or make us swallow things we don't want to. Our abuser leaves us with cuts, bruises and broken bones, and at worst they may even kill us.

Although we may know it's wrong to stay in an abusive relationship, we may be too scared, and too lacking in confidence, to leave. If our partner is physically abusing us, they may also use financial or emotional abuse to keep us in the relationship.

No one has the right to hurt us, threaten us, blackmail us or violate our rights to money, safety, freedom and independence.

Domestic violence and physical abuse are complex, painful and damaging experiences. As well as physical harm the results of abuse can affect our mind, we may develop anxiety or depression.

We stay in abusive relationships for all kinds of reasons; we may have been physically abused as children or brought up where violence was "okay". We may believe that a violent relationship is all we deserve, and we may confuse violence with love.

The effect of being violent is often ignored and is equally damaging. Over time, without an effective curb being put on their behaviour, the violent individual inevitably increases the degree of violence they use.

If we're experiencing domestic abuse or a violent crime of some kind, help and support is available.

The police can help us deal with the immediate situation and support us in getting a court injunction. But if we fear that going to the cops might escalate the problem, at the back of this book there's a list of the many organisations who can help with support, advice and listening.

Both adults and children are affected by physical abuse; the effects of seeing, hearing or sensing violence can be just as damaging as receiving the blows.

Time may be a great healer, but it's also a lousy beautician!
Anon

Physis

The Greeks believed that all living things have an innate drive to heal and repair. Physis is our natural drive to health, something each of has whether we know it or not.

Everything that happens to us can enhance our life, depending on how we use and view the experience. If we're able to learn from the lessons of the past, the wisdom we gain can inform what comes next (not sure about our afterlife – yet!).

Sometimes it's hard to learn from life.

Many of us get caught up in repetitive patterns and dysfunctional behaviour, meeting familiar triggers with the same responses which lead to the same old outcome – "Why does this always happen to me?"

"Life is a process of becoming, a combination of states we have to go through. Where people fail is that they wish to elect a state and remain in it. This is a kind of death." Anais Nin

As we explore our patterns and programming, we can begin to do things differently.

The talking therapies can speed up our natural drive towards health and healing; as we talk through our issues and recognise the patterns, the problems can melt away.

Postnatal depression (PND)

PND is particularly distressing because most women look forward to meeting their baby and being a mum. Instead we feel depressed, as though we can't cope. We may feel guilty about feeling like this.

Postnatal depression can go on for weeks or months. Some of us may experience it mildly, but for some it's more extreme. If we have PND we tend to feel tired or irritable all the time, we may have trouble sleeping, and we feel low, unhappy, unable to access loving feelings. We may feel anxious or overwhelmed, or become overanxious about our baby. We may find it hard to connect with our partner and be uninterested in sexual intimacy.

Postnatal depression is triggered by many things. Our body goes through an extraordinary experience from birth to breast-feeding and the changes in our hormone levels can affect our mood.

We may experience PND as a response to relationship difficulties, the medical management of the birthgiving process (like post-operative depression), the stresses and strains of money or housing, or if our baby is born prematurely or has been poorly. If we've been depressed before, or lost our own mother while we were small, we might be more prone to it

PND is very common and very treatable; we can talk to our doctor or find support from a counsellor. Though medication doesn't cure it, it can ease the symptoms whilst we explore our situation and imbalance. A small percentage of new mums may experience postpartum psychosis, a serious mood disorder affecting our sense of reality, at worst if untreated it can lead to suicide and infanticide. It's rare and can develop within weeks of birth and should be treated immediately. The sooner we seek treatment, the sooner we can get better.

1 in 10 women in the UK will experience postnatal depression after having a baby.

Post-traumatic stress disorder

Post-traumatic stress disorder (PTSD) is the delayed re-experience of a psychological trauma. It's a relatively new mental health term. Recently, medical and mental health professionals have become aware of the affects of trauma and how it can debilitate those who've experienced it and affect the lives of others around them.

If we experience PTSD it's because we've had an experience we find horrifying – we've witnessed the atrocities of war or a traumatic disaster, or have experienced sexual and/or physical abuse. PTSD can be caused by any event where we experience extreme fear, horror and/or helplessness.

With PTSD we experience distressing memories and/or flashbacks for some time, maybe years, after the traumatic event. We may need to avoid people or places that provoke memories or feelings we think we can't cope with.

We may feel numb all the time, unable to access positive feelings. We may lose interest in life or social activities. We may find it hard to sleep, concentrate or hold down a job. At worst we can develop depression or dissociation.

PTSD can be treated. Some of us may need medication to help with the extreme symptoms associate with the condition. Nothing can take away the memory of a traumatic experience, but with time and talking we can come to terms with the effects on us of these events. We may find sharing our ordeal with a counsellor helpful, as this may help to release the emotional energy that's been trapped in us by the trauma.

Self-help groups are available to those with PTSD. If working in the armed forces or emergency services, trauma is something faced every day; employers and a number of organisations can offer post event debriefing and more specialised support if needed.

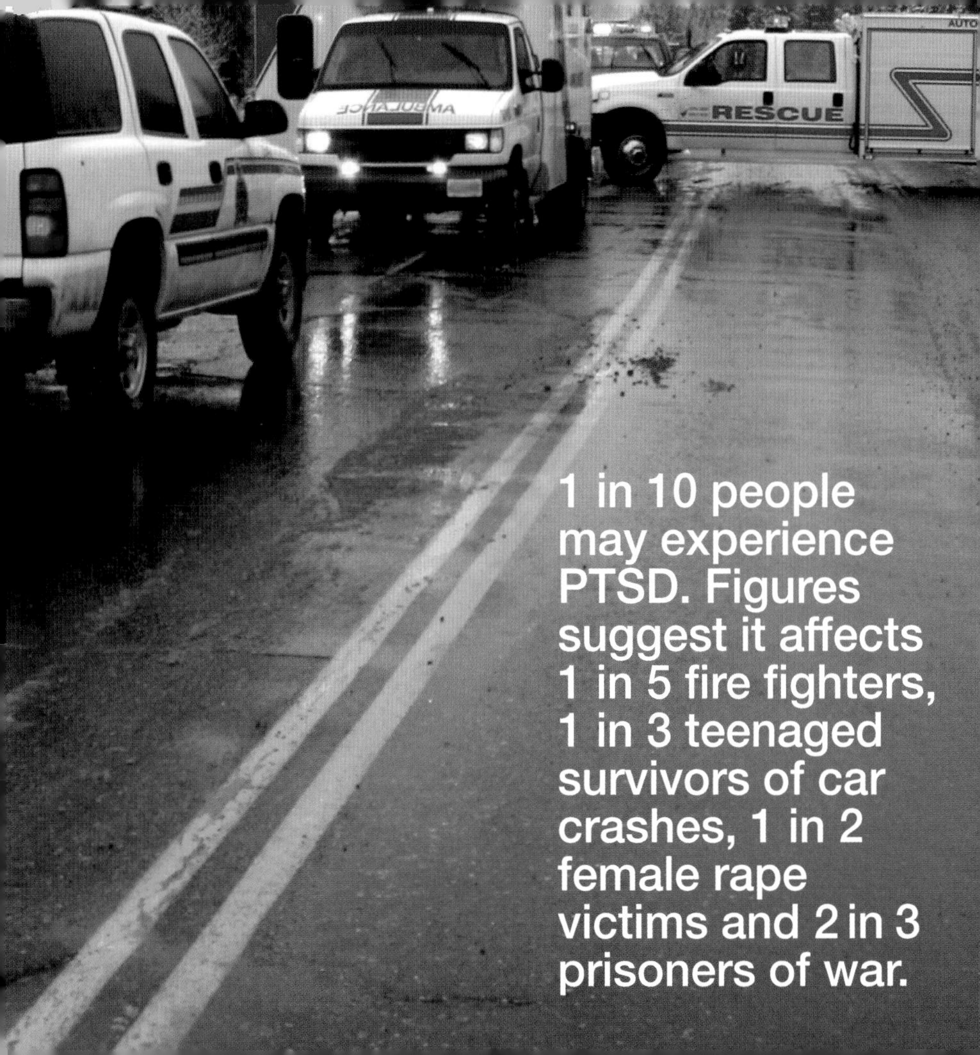

1 in 10 people may experience PTSD. Figures suggest it affects 1 in 5 fire fighters, 1 in 3 teenaged survivors of car crashes, 1 in 2 female rape victims and 2 in 3 prisoners of war.

P

Pre-conscious

The pre-conscious part of our mind sits somewhere between the conscious and the unconscious. It's the place where we store short-term memory items which, though not fully in the conscious, can be accessed quickly – things like telephone numbers, shopping lists and directions to places.

Prejudice

Prejudices are fixed beliefs we have about others or the outside world. These beliefs are learned and are often accompanied by a reluctance to update or renew them.

"Common sense is merely the deposit of prejudice laid down in the human mind before the age of 18."
Albert Einstein

We can remain stuck in our prejudices as a way of complying with the teachings of our parents or caregivers. But if we want to, we can choose to reject old beliefs; to begin with, it's easier to do this if we replace them with new ones, but as we develop we may find that we need fewer beliefs in order to be comfortable in ourselves.

"Prejudice is a burden that confuses the past, threatens the future and renders the present inaccessible."
Maya Angelou

We will all have developed prejudices of one kind or another. By their very nature, our prejudices are pre-judgements – they are the values and beliefs we bring to a situation, sometimes without even being aware that we're doing this.

Prejudices are a distortion of the way we see the world, and they can cause a great deal of harm or conflict – to ourselves, to others and to the world itself.

Prejudices can be cultural as well as individual; they affect our attitudes to race, sexuality, religion and gender. At times in life, we may need to explore some of our prejudices – we can all learn how to greet a situation or individual with an open mind.

Procrastination

"The organizational meeting of the procrastination club has been put off until next week!" Anon

Procrastination is about putting things off. We all do it from time to time … it's an avoidance tactic, but we may also procrastinate – wisely sometimes – if we're lacking in the knowledge or information needed for us to make a decision.

When we procrastinate to avoid, we miss opportunities to resolve inner issues because they cause conflict or pain in our head.

"Know the true value of time; snatch, seize, and enjoy every moment of it. No idleness, no laziness, no procrastination: never put off till to-morrow what you can do to-day." Lord Chesterfield

We procrastinate if we want to avoid confrontation, decision-making, change or progress.

We may want to move forward, but instead we feel blocked – we may fear change, or we may not have discovered the inner resources or capabilities we have to tackle a situation with courage and confidence.

We can share our procrastination tendencies with a counsellor. When we find we can gently explore what we had felt we couldn't face, it soon appears less scary!

"If you had to identify in a single word the reason why the human race has not achieved, and never will achieve, its full potential, that word would be 'meetings'." Dave Barry

Psyche

"No excellent soul is exempt from a mixture of madness."
Aristotle

The word psyche was used by the Greeks over 2,500 years ago to describe what we know as our soul.

"You don't have a soul. You are a Soul. You have a body."
C.S. Lewis

Nowadays it's a term used to describe the mind (which still, to some, is the soul).

"Ordinary riches can be stolen, real riches cannot. In your soul are infinitely precious things that cannot be taken from you."
Oscar Wilde

Psychiatry

Psychiatry is a medical specialism that involves diagnosing mental disorders and prescribing medication to prevent the disorders from causing disturbance in our life and those around us.

A psychiatrist holds a MD degree – the letters should be present after a psychiatrist's name.

Traditionally, psychiatry has taken the view that all mental disorders are medical rather than emotional or behavioural. Psychiatrists are mostly involved at the hospital end of things helping those of us with long term or acute experiences of mental illness.

Our doctor may also refer us to a psychiatrist because they specialise in the medical treatment of mental illness.

Isn't it a bit unnerving that doctors call what they do "practice?"

As well as prescribing more specific medication for our condition or brain chemical imbalance, a psychiatrists can also help us longer term ensuring we are on the right rehabilitation or treatment programme and/or have support from a community psychiatric nurse.

These days psychiatrists work more holistically; exploring the many social, psychological, emotional and behavioural issues that can lead to mental dis-ease and routes to recovery.

Psychiatrists have been referred to as "shrinks"; though there's no real history for the development of this word it could be linked to an Amazonian tribe. "Headshrinkers" refers to the Jivaro tribe who pickled the heads of their enemies. They removed the skull from inside the skin, and what was left would in time shrink to the size of a human fist (nice, eh?). But psychiatrists work to heal our minds, not shrink them!

Psychoanalysis

The term "psychoanalysis" is most strongly associated with the work of Sigmund Freud, but also refers to a body of theories and techniques that provide a framework for understanding the mind and human behaviour.

Psychoanalytic theory suggests that our early life experiences, before we are seven years old, create the template for how we get on later in life.

Psychoanalysis and psychotherapy encourage us to go back over some of our early experiences. We can develop an understanding and gain insight into ourselves from the past.

Having done this we can, given time, change ourselves, or at least come to terms with what we did or didn't get – but only when we've found out what we learned at a deep level from our carers.

Carl Jung, Alfred Adler, Melanie Klein and many other doctors and psychoanalysts have contributed to the theories in this field.

Psychology

The term "psychology" refers to the study of the mind and behaviour. It can be applied to any living organism – animal or human life, and it's a massive topic – far too big for this little book. But it contains a lot of knowledge and information gained from psychology!

Psychosexual development

Psychoanalytic theory suggests that how we experience the first seven years of our life creates the template for what happens later.

Sigmund Freud believed early life could be seen in five phases, and that if we weren't supported through each of those stages to fulfil our needs in them, we develop tendencies to fulfil them within ourselves as adults.

Freud named each stage: oral, anal, phallic, latent and genital (sounds fascinating!).

Each stage outlines both our physical and psychic development, and according to him, if we don't complete each phase successfully, we can reach adult life incomplete in some way. This can lead to dependency or a need to control; we may not trust others or find intimacy difficult to achieve.

The oral stage takes place between birth and 18 months. During this time we're entirely dependent on others, and our psychic energy is driven towards getting our needs met. We experience pleasure (or not in some cases) through sucking and feeding.

If we're fulfilled at this stage and feel safe and secure, we can move on to the next – but if our needs weren't met or we were over-pleasured, we may not trust others, or can find life hard. Life doesn't always give us what we want (although, looking at the bigger picture, it may give us what we need …but that's outside the scope of this book).

Our level of dependency is determined during our oral development. If we're abandoned or neglected, it's likely we'll develop some kind of dependency, or find it hard, as an adult, to be interdependent, and may resort to codependency.

The anal stage takes place between 18 months and 3½ years. The physical focus is on our anus (nice). During this time we learn about control – not just our bladder or bum, but also how to control our behaviour and impulses. If our parents and caregivers continually overcontrol or undercontrol us, we may develop control issues later.

The phallic stage takes place between 3½ and 6 years old. During this time the physical focus is on the penis (or, according to Freud, lack of one if we're girls). At this stage, we explore our gender and genitals!

As we develop our sexual feelings, we direct them towards our opposite-sex parent (if we've got one – and if we haven't, this can cause us problems). Because these feelings aren't socially acceptable, they can, Freud said, turn to hostility or fear; boys fear castration and girls experience "penis envy".

Our experiences during this part of our development will determine how we feel about our sexuality, our sexual attitudes and behaviour as adults.

During the latency stage – between 6 and 16 – our development tends to slow down. Our impulses settle, and the psychosexual conflict we experience eases off (thank goodness for that, then!).

The genital stage takes place towards the end of and after puberty. This phase is about maturity and creativity, not just making babies! During the genital stage of our life we explore our personal development and find ways to release our creative force.

Freud believed that if we navigate each stage in a healthy and supported way, we reach adult life balanced and whole, able to love and able to work. But that if en route our needs weren't met, we may reach adulthood with issues outstanding.

Psychosis

"Doubt is to certainty as neurosis is to psychosis. The neurotic is in doubt and has fears about persons and things; the psychotic has convictions and makes claims about them. In short, the neurotic has problems, the psychotic has solutions." Thomas Szasz.

The term "psychosis" describes the out-of-the-ordinary experiences we have when we hear or see things that don't fit with the perceptions of others, or the beliefs we have that don't fit into our culture. Psychosis affects our sense of reality; our thoughts dart about, we can't concentrate and we lack insight or awareness as to our real state of mind.

Psychosis can be triggered by physical dis-ease such as malaria, flu or extreme changes in our blood sugar levels. Excessive drinking and drug taking can lead to psychotic experiences, and cannabis has been linked to the condition.

Psychotic experiences involve a chemical change in the brain: an imbalance in our dopamine levels can affect our attention and perception. Antipsychotic medication works to correct our dopamine level.

Other mental dis-ease such as depression, schizophrenia, postnatal depression and bipolar disorder can also trigger psychotic episodes.

Some experts believe our childhood experiences may make us more prone to psychosis. If our parents or caregivers were overcritical or overprotective, we may be more vulnerable to it.

Some therapists believe psychosis is the expression of mind-releasing painful or forbidden thoughts and feelings. It can be hard to talk about psychotic experiences, as we may fear we'll be judged or labelled a loon. Medication can help in the short term with the symptoms of psychosis, and talking through what our mind's making known to us can help us cope longer term.

Psychosomatic

"Psychosomatic" means linked to the mind. Some believe all disease starts in our mind, others believe it's all to do with our body (excluding the mind), and a few believe that it's often generated by the two together.

If our mind is overloaded or we're not coping well, we may develop rashes, psoriasis, asthma, eczema or migraine. These symptoms are physical responses to an unhappy head – we don't have them all the time, and they're triggered by our state of mind.

Contrary to what some people would have us believe, our mind is part of our body; what we experience psychologically will affect us physically. Stress is just one example of our body coping when our head's under pressure.

If we experience a psychosomatic condition, we can talk to our doctor. We may decide to take medication to relieve symptoms. Longer term, we can explore what triggers our illness.

If we can get to the true root of the problem, we can cure ourselves. The challenge is finding that root!

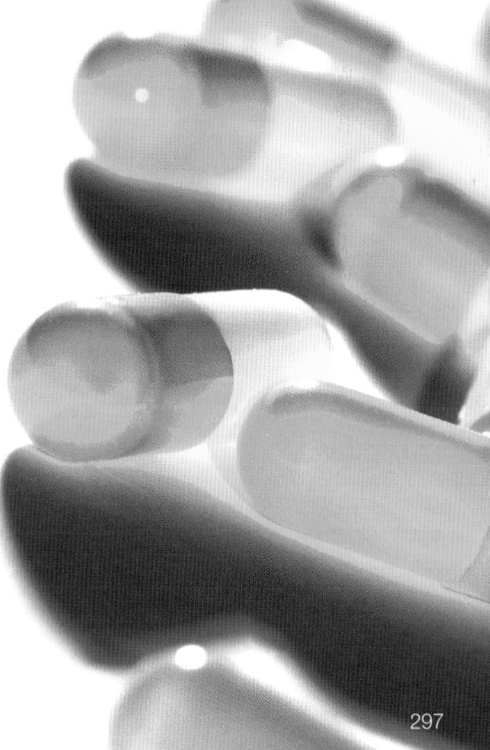

Recognition

"There are two things people want more than sex and money... recognition and praise." Mary Kay Ash

Abraham Maslow developed what's known as the "hierarchy of needs". He believed that whilst our physical survival depends on food, water, shelter and warmth, for psychological development our No.1 need is "recognition".

We all need to be recognised. From childhood, we all need validation and recognition for who we are and what we do. We need recognition that we exist, that we're here, we're valued and we're important. Recognition comes from others – and whether it's negative or positive, it's a basic need. In the absence of positive recognition, we absorb the negative.

The recognition we received from adults while we were small teaches us to value ourselves – or not, as the case may be.

What we were taught to believe about ourselves will have influenced what we've become. What we hear later we make match those beliefs … do we appreciate compliments and believe we're great? Or do we ignore praise?

Sometimes we take ourselves and our life for granted. How often do we say "I'm so glad I'm here", "I love and like you just as you are"?

The more we celebrate and appreciate our life, the richer we'll feel and the more abundance we'll see.

As we recognise ourselves, so we recognise others. We're all connected through our need for recognition.

"Love is but the discovery of ourselves in others, and the delight in the recognition."
Alexander Smith

Regression

According to Sigmund Freud, regression is one of our psychological defence mechanisms.

Rather than dealing with a situation in a mature way, we temporarily revert to behaviour or feelings associated with our childhood (hiding under the duvet indeed!).

Regression is particularly common in stressful or traumatic situations. Some events cause us to access a painful, frustrating or difficult memory that we've pushed to the back of our mind.

As we become aware of what triggers our childhood issues or emotional pain, we can work through the past and release our regression.

We learn to step back from a situation, detach ourselves from it, and take our time to respond or react.

Some forms of regression are healthy!

It's important to be in touch with the childlike part of us, so that we can still feel wonder and joy with the world. We all need to be playful, excited and feel free, and we can all be creative and access our inner child.

As we enjoy being with our own children, we can feel childlike again but whether we're parents or not no matter how old we are, we're still a child at heart!

Rehabilitation/treatment centres

If we're experiencing addiction or career burnout, or have had a breakdown of some kind, we may choose to spend some time in a treatment centre as either a residential patient or an outpatient.

Private treatment centres are different from mental health units, dealing more specifically with addiction or overload. If our habit is endangering our health or we can no longer take part in day-to-day life, and if we've got the money, we can pay to stay at a clinic. The Priory is one of the most famous clinics in the UK.

Some treatment centres are free, funded by local authorities, the NHS or charitable donations. There are free treatment centres all over the UK. Some are open for visits during office hours, some during the night, and some are residential.

Most of the free treatment centres deal specifically with drug or alcohol addiction, and run support groups or offer counselling and advice. If we want to recover from addiction, we can enrol ourselves into these centres, or be referred by our doctor.

The Priory Hospital, Roehampton, is Britain's oldest private psychiatric hospital. It used to be a stately home, today it's owned by the Priory Group who have some 50 clinics worldwide.

A week at the Priory costs about £3640; paying patients have included many well known celebrities,musicians, performers and artists. It just goes to show that anyone and everyone can experience and with support overcome emotional or psychological difficulties.

Rejection

"We can't be rejected if we fully accept ourselves."
Darren Bottrill

Rejection is one of the largest sources of emotional pain. If we were repeatedly rejected as children – ignored, abused or unable to be vulnerable or express our true selves – it's likely rejection will be an issue for us later.

If the adults in our life couldn't or didn't make themselves available to us when we were small, as adults we'll find it hard to be available to ourselves. Rejection can result in us feeling unacceptable, unlovable and unworthy.

As adults, we may also find it hard to be supportive with ourselves, or indeed with others. We learned that to be vulnerable or open about how we felt led to rejection, hurt or shame. We were unable to be close and intimate.

As adults, we may find ourselves consciously or unconsciously setting ourselves up for rejection. The unconscious part of our mind is trying to heal or resolve rejection from the past.

We may find it helpful to explore these patterns and feelings with a counsellor, because as we heal old hurts old habits will soon fall away, and we learn to approach the problems in an adult way rather than in a childlike manner.

Who hasn't experienced a rejection of some kind or another? It hurts – but the more intimate and supportive we are within, the more we can be available to, and accepting of, ourselves.

"Human beings, like plants, grow in the soil of acceptance, not in the atmosphere of rejection." John Powell

Relationships

"In your relationships with others, remember the basic and critically important rule: If you want to be loved, be lovable." Anon.

Relationships can give us some of life's most meaningful experiences, but the single most important relationship is the one we have within. Just like our relationships with others, our relationship within is important.

How we relate to ourselves is likely to mirror and influence how we relate to others.

Relationships come and go, but the one within is the one that will last (until we pop our clogs that is – but who knows?).

A healthy relationship within is part of a healthy mind. It's important we hold ourselves in high regard, that we feel connected to ourselves.

As we develop a stronger relationship to ourselves, we feel and know we can support ourselves without needing to depend on others.

As we grow our relationships grow. We can become more intimate with friends and partners, and as we understand ourselves, we'll understand them; as we accept who we are, we accept others (life's a lot easier when we're not trying to change everyone).

We can all learn how to develop a stronger relationship within. Just being quiet with ourselves or exploring who we are in therapy can help foster and strengthen our inner connection. The more we know ourselves, the more we can be there and support who we are. We cannot love another until we learn to love ourselves.

"People often say that this or that person has not yet found himself. But the self is not something one finds, it is something one creates." Thomas Szasz

Our relationships with others can be the source of our pleasure and also our pain. We have all kinds of relationships – and not just with people; we have relationships with our pets, animals, nature, food and drink (and sometimes our pillow – ahhh!).

Our relationship to others and the world around us can act as a mirror; what goes on in our interactions outside often reflects where we're at within. If our relationships are happy, healthy, open and nurturing, it's because that's the way we are. If our relationships are unhappy, hurtful or abusive, then we need to ask the question – why are we in them? All our relationships affect our mind.

"Don't let people drive you crazy when you know it's in walking distance." Anon

Sometimes we attract unhealthy relationships because we're looking to others to make us feel whole, to complete our self-worth and make us feel good. When that person leaves, we feel even worse.

"In any relationship in which two people become one, the end result is two half people." Wayne Dyer

Most of us have a variety of relationships in our life. Different relationships require different ways of relating, and how we are with our lover is likely to be different from the way we relate to a colleague or co-worker. We feel close to some and not so with others. Some relationships involve commitment, some just come and go – but it's the one within that matters the most!

Relationship counselling

If we're experiencing problems in our relationships, either as part of a couple or as a member of a family, we might find it helpful to work through our difficulties with a trained counsellor or therapist.

Between April 2006 and 2007, Relate ran over 250,000 hours of counselling with nearly 100,000 people throughout the UK.

The talking therapies can be a help if we want to explore, understand and improve our relationships.

It's not a counsellor or therapists job to take sides, give advice or comment on the nature of our relationships, but rather to help us reach a new understanding of both ourselves and our loved ones.

For any relationship to work, both individuals need to be whole and healthy in themselves to begin with and this starts within.

Even though we are part of a couple, we may find it helpful to work individually on ourselves as a way to improve our relationships. For others of us going together to couples counselling can help too.

Whether individually or together, counselling can help us explore and understand the issues and insights we take into our relationships. We can learn to understand the dynamics of our relationships and why we're facing the challenges we are.

Relate has nearly 2,000 trained therapists working all over the UK.

Relate, formerly known as the Marriage Guidance Council, is the UK's largest relationship counselling body and there are many individual therapists outside Relate who are trained to work with couples.

Between 2006
and 2007, Relate
have helped over
5000 individuals
overcome sexual
problems.

Sadness

Sadness is a core authentic feeling most associated with the past.

We often feel sad when we look back or reflect on the past.

Sadness is evoked by many life experiences: loss, bereavement and endings, the end of a relationship, the end of a holiday or the end of project. When happy events come to an end, we sometimes feel sad.

"Anger is just a cowardly extension of sadness. It's a lot easier to be angry at someone than it is to tell them you're hurt." Tom Gates

It's funny (well not really, 'cause we're exploring sadness) but sadness is sometimes hard to express. Just as with fear or anger, we bottle up sadness – we pack it away rather than release the emotional energy at the time it arises.

At times in our life we may need to explore and release old feelings of sadness. We may need to give ourselves time to grieve and heal, and we may not realise how much sadness we're holding onto.

Grieving allows our mind and body to process feelings of sadness, and then, as we release sad feelings, we've more room for happiness in both our heads and our hearts.

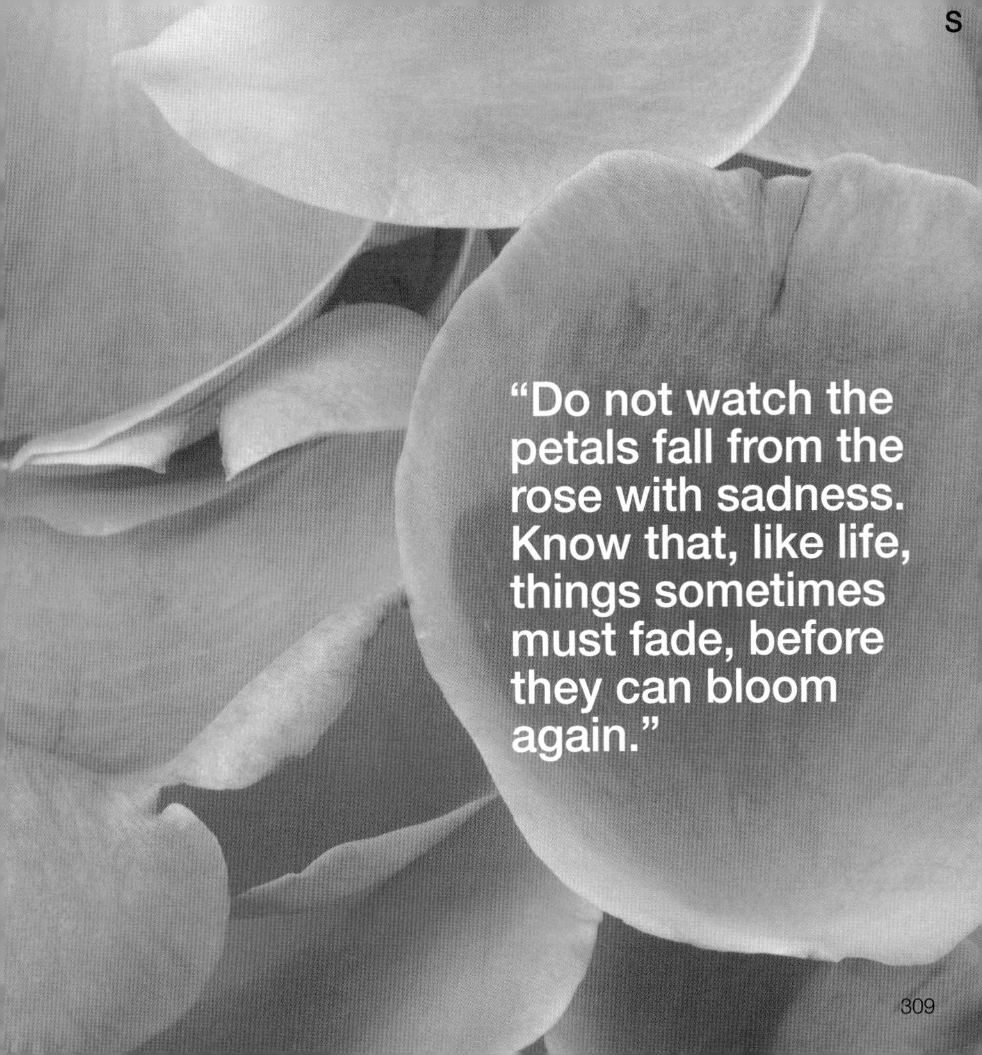
"Do not watch the
petals fall from the
rose with sadness.
Know that, like life,
things sometimes
must fade, before
they can bloom
again."

Schizophrenia

"Schizophrenia" is a term to describe a condition that's well known and sometimes feared, it has many stigmas attached to it and is often misunderstood. Fundamentally, it's an illness of the brain, it's no one's fault and whilst society often attributes violence to schizophrenia, it is more like that the person suffering the condition will harm themselves rather than others.

Doctors often describe schizophrenia as a form of psychosis; in their view a schizophrenic can't distinguish their own thoughts from reality (i.e. the shared perceptions, ideas and values that the people in the schizophrenic's culture hold as real).

As well as having a distorted sense of reality, we may hear voices in our heads, and we may believe that someone else is inside our mind controlling our thoughts, we may believe these voices to be real.

Today, experts view schizophrenia a holistic way, treating the individual as much as the illness. The symptoms we display as a schizophrenic are often logical, natural reactions to distressing life events.

If we have the condition we're likely to display drastic and extreme changes in our behaviour. We may become anxious and confused, and suspicious of those who don't agree with our perceptions; we may feel that we don't need help at all. It's a hard condition to diagnose, as many other mental illnesses include similar symptoms.

With schizophrenia, psychiatrists look for particular things: strange thinking, hallucinations, delusions, emotional flatness, apathy or difficulties with concentration. If we experience the condition, we may want to avoid social situations or feel an intense need to be protected.

Mind state that around 1 in every 100 people in the UK is diagnosed with schizophrenia… It affects men and women in roughly the same numbers.

Some argue that schizophrenia is learned, and there's little research to confirm it's genetic. Our early life experiences can be such that we're more prone to experience the condition.

The brain chemical dopamine may be linked to schizophrenia; medication used to treat the condition targets the dopamine levels in our head.

Some research and personal statements suggest that stressful, distressing or life-changing events like homelessness, poverty, unemployment, the loss of a loved one, and sexual, physical, emotional or racial abuse are contributing factors in developing the illness.

Research has concluded that cannabis and illegal street drugs can result in schizophrenia.

And if we already have it, taking cannabis, cocaine or amphetamines can make it worse.

Some evidence suggests that physical factors or an injury to the brain can be linked to schizophrenia, but most experts believe it's an illness and combination of things.

There are – so far – no concrete answers as to why some people develop it and others don't. However, if we do experience schizophrenia, experts believe the sooner we get treatment the better. Early diagnosed and intervention is believed to be the best road to managing our illness.

If we experience schizophrenia or know someone who does, there is help and support available. A psychiatrist can help us, they are able to diagnose the condition and prescribe medication which can be very affective in treating this illness including the symptoms of delusions, hearing voices or racing thoughts.

S

Seasonal affective disorder

The sun is a natural thermonuclear reactor. It burns at some 6,000 million kilowatts, and we feel its heat though it's some 150 million miles away!

Who doesn't feel better when the sun is shining? Or lower when it's not? SAD affects most of us to some extent or another, most of us tending to feel less exuberant in the winter.

SAD is a mild form of depression or a low mood associated with lack of sunlight. It's mostly experienced during the winter months, if we've a history of depression, SAD can exacerbate the symptoms.

If we experience SAD there's lots we can do for ourselves. Research suggests that using anti-SAD lamps and lights for a certain number of hours a day can ease our winter blues. We can get out in the sunshine too.

Sunny days in winter are often clearer and brighter than the hazy, lazy days of summer.

Eating a proper balanced diet can help us; eating properly, regularly and frequently can help keep our blood sugar level steady, helping our mood and energy levels.

We may need to watch how much booze we consume (it's no good staying in, hugging a bottle of red wine); alcohol in large and all too regular amounts can act as a mild depressant.

Grabbing what sunlight we can will help us with SAD.

Sunlight increases our serotonin levels. Research suggests that it stimulates the pineal gland, a pea-sized organ at the centre of the brain. This gland creates a chemical known as tryptamine or melatonin, which runs our body clock and is sensitive to the seasons. Getting out in the sunshine increases our tryptamine levels, helping us feel better in summer and winter!

S

Self-esteem

Self-esteem is about how we value ourselves – our sense of worth. Do we feel worthy and deserving of love? Do we feel we deserve to be heard, respected and supported? Do we feel we deserve to be happy and succeed?

Our self-esteem is about feeling good about ourselves. When we feel good about ourselves, we do good to ourselves.

Self-esteem is a about feeling as well as thinking. Very often we know we're worthy, but sometimes we don't feel it. Our sense of self-worth starts in childhood (like most things, it seems).

How we feel about ourselves and how we value our being is something we learned from adults while young. If we were constantly criticised, rejected or abused as children, it will affect how we feel about ourselves as adults.

"The strongest single factor in prosperity consciousness is self-esteem: believing you can do it, believing you deserve it, believing you will get it." Jerry Gillies

Self-esteem, like confidence, is something we can learn and develop. We can learn to love ourselves and feel good about who we are, and the more we do what makes us feel good, the better we'll feel inside.

Outdated beliefs or unresolved hurts can get in the way of our source of self-love. We may need to explore and release old emotions or develop new beliefs about our worth and value. With time and commitment, we can soon learn to love ourselves more. (We're all we have, after all!).

Self-harm

We self-harm when we intentionally injure or hurt ourselves. It can involve cutting ourselves, taking overdoses, throwing or punching ourselves against something, pulling out our hair or eyelashes, and picking or burning our skin, as well as sniffing harmful substances.

Self-harm is most common amongst young people; some do it regularly, some once or twice … it's a way to release emotional pain. Few who self-harm go on to commit suicide, because it's a way of coping with life rather than wanting to end it. If we self-harm, we may have experienced painful relationships, we may have been bullied.

We may self-harm because we've lost someone close to us. We may have been neglected or experienced lack of love from our parents or caregivers. Sexual, emotional and physical abuse can also lead to self-harm, and sometimes having a serious illness can affect us, too.

Self-harm becomes a means by which we deal with painful feelings; these feelings can be triggered by family life, school or peer group pressure. We may have low self-esteem or feel bad about our bodies, and we may not have learned to love ourselves (yet!).

If feelings of anger, self-hatred, shame, guilt, sadness or hopelessness become too much to bear, we harm ourselves to release their effects.

Young people can be trusted to overcome self-harm themselves: pressure from adults can exacerbate it. It's important we're allowed to decide for ourselves what support or treatment we might need. We can talk to our doctor, a supportive teacher, or adult we trust and feel safe with. We may find a youth worker or counsellor helpful too.

If we've been abused or mistreated by adults or care givers, we may find it hard to trust adults to help and support us as we work through our problems.

Above all, the first step is to accept we need help. There are many organisations who can help young people and adults understand self-harm. They can help us explore why we do it and give us support as we overcome some of the difficulties we may be facing. Many young people find the email service: jo@samaritans.org useful.

Self-sabotage

Self-sabotage is action that is driven by unconscious beliefs.

Self-sabotage isn't about lack of skills, abilities or effort. Instead, it comes from the depths of our mind. Deep-held unconscious beliefs are often stronger than our conscious mind, so they influence and sabotage our efforts to do, have or say what we want.

Self-sabotage is bit like a game of tug-of-war, but the game goes on in our head rather than at the school fête!

Self-sabotage is driven by the unconscious and by learned messages. Often, just as we go for what we want in life, we hear a little voice saying "no, you mustn't do that", "you shouldn't have that", or "it's bad to do that". That voice is our inner critic; the things it says have been learned from our parents, teachers and caregivers.

As adults, we're perfectly capable of make our own choices. Most of us know, most of the time, what's good or right for us. We all have the capacity to go for what we want, but can find it hard when the critic kicks in.

Self-sabotage can lead to frustration; we may feel de-motivated, as though our confidence and sense of self-worth has diminished. If we allow ourselves to self-sabotage, we can end up destroying relationships or new opportunities.

As we explore and learn to understand our capacity to sabotage ourselves, we can learn to ignore or replace the messages from our inner critic with healthier, supportive and permitting words.

Affirmation: I deserve success and happiness.

Serotonin

Serotonin is an important brain chemical. It's a neurotransmitter that regulates body temperature, appetite and our metabolism. It's associated with feeling anger and with our sexuality. It also stimulates vomiting (nice!).

Serotonin is a hormone made by the brain; certain foods, like chicken and turkey, contain chemicals that help us create it.

Serotonin is the chemical most associated with feeling good; it's a mood regulator and helps us keep our bodies under control. It helps us sleep and feel calm, and can relieve depression.

Some research suggests that serotonin is involved in the process of chemical addiction. If our serotonin levels are low we don't feel good, and so, though it's temporary and often harmful, we may develop a chemical dependency to restore a good feeling.

Serotonin affects how we feel. If we've been exposed to long-term stress or high levels of stress, the level of serotonin in our body can drop, leading to mild or even severe forms of depression. Seasonal affective disorder is linked to low serotonin levels.

Some antidepressants are specifically designed to target how the brain creates and uses serotonin; they're known as SSRIs – selective serotonin re-uptake inhibitors (see p.38).

Sexual abuse

Sexual abuse is the involvement of under-age or developmentally immature children in sexual activity with adults. The same violation can take place between adults where sexual acts take place without consent.

If as children we were abused, we were unable to truly comprehend the violation that happened to us, and we were certainly unable to give informed consent to acts that violate the social "norms" of family roles.

"If those who told us they loved us abused us as children, it can be terrifying to love again." Marilyn Jope

Sexual abuse can run in families for generations. Adult family members who should be trustworthy often perpetuate sexual abuse. Sexual abuse can range from severe life-threatening acts to warm and sensual contact laden with shame, guilt and a fear of exposure.

The effects of sexual abuse are many. It can lead to addiction and self-abuse in later life, lack of trust, depression, anxiety, low self-esteem, over-alertness, passivity, difficulties in concentration, poor body image, sexual difficulties or dysfunction and inappropriate sexual maturity, and these can in turn lead to further abuse.

Our sexuality is a precious, intimate, personal part of ourselves. If we were violated sexually as children, the effects can be deep and long lasting. We may be left feeling guilty, as if it was our fault, and we may feel ashamed of who we are.

The affects of abuse severely distort our state of mind.

Trained therapists, especially those who work in the field of abuse, can offer us support, compassion and a non-judgemental space where we can, in time, work through these painful experiences and begin to feel better about ourselves.

Sexuality

Our sexuality is about who we are, and how we feel about ourselves in a sexual sense including our gender, sexual orientation and sexual preferences.

How we validate and express our sexuality is important to our state of mind. We're all sexual beings, and if we repress or disregard the sexual part of us, it can affect how we value and express ourselves.

Our sexuality is part of our physical, emotional and intellectual make-up. How we connect to our sexual selves is important. How we regard and integrate our sexuality into the whole of our being can reinforce and strengthen our sense of identity and individuality.

"One is not born a woman, one becomes one."
Simone de Beauvoir

Our sexual expression, and the thoughts and feelings we hold towards our sexuality, will be

There's no right or wrong – we're all different, and there's no such thing as "normal".

We can express our sexuality in many ways – what we wear and how we wear it, how we experience the sensual pleasures in life and how we take care of ourselves, including our sexual health.

Do we respect and enjoy our bodies? How do we feel about our sense of touch and physical connection to others? As we become more in touch with our sexuality, this can increase our sexual awareness.

As we grow and develop, the views we hold about our sexuality may also change. How we felt about ourselves sexually as teenagers may be different to how we feel now.

Lots of things affect our sexuality: our sexual preferences, our attitudes towards our gender and our sexual orientation as well as hormones and age

Our spiritual values or religious beliefs can also inform our sense of sexuality and what this part of us means within.

"In itself, homosexuality is as limiting as heterosexuality: the ideal should be to be capable of loving a woman or a man; either, a human being, without feeling fear, restraint, or obligation."
Simone de Beauvoir

The attitudes we hold towards our sexuality were learned. As children we were taught how to think, feel and relate to our bodies, but what we learned then may no longer be relevant. Adults and teachers may have given us approving or disapproving messages about our sexuality – but for us as adults, it's our sexuality, not theirs.

Our sexuality is an intrinsic part of us. Some of us may feel ashamed of it, especially if we have been abused or violated in this way.

We might be experiencing difficulties in expressing, exploring or coming to terms with our sexual orientation.

If our sexual expression or sexual orientation is causing confusion within us, it's something we can explore with a therapist or counsellor. There are many talking professionals who are trained to work with the issues associated with sex and sexuality.

Our sense of who we are sexually is intimate, a delicate and tender part of ourselves – but as we begin to understand and validate our sexuality, it can enhance our sense of identity.

We can develop the way we enjoy and share ourselves in a sexual, sensual sense. We can all learn healthier and happier ways to celebrate life as sexual beings, whether we've got a partner or not.

Affirmation: I can express myself sexually, enjoy and feel good in my body.

Shame

"I used to look in the mirror and feel shame, I look in the mirror now and I absolutely love myself." Drew Barrymore

Shame is a powerful feeling that differs from guilt. We feel guilt because of something we've done, whereas shame is felt because of who we are. It's often linked to fear – fear of rejection or abandonment.

Shame is an inauthentic feeling, often imposed by others - we're taught or learn to feel ashamed of ourselves. When we're born we're far from shameful, it's a feeling we learn through our interactions with adults, parents, teachers and caregivers.

Why we feel shame depends on how we were scolded for the things we did or said while small. Often, as children, we get told off for being ourselves. If we're told off for being just as we are, it's likely we'll feel ashamed... simply because we exist!

Shame is sometimes associated with our sense of sexuality. The natural process of discovering who we are sexually often gives rise to shame, especially if our elders gave us disapproving messages about masturbation, sex and sexual expression.

If we experienced sexual shame during our childhood, then when we reach adult life the sexual side of ourselves may be welded to feelings of fear, shame and low self-worth.

If we've been sexually, physically or emotionally abused, as an adult or as a child, it can lead to shame. We may feel as though we were responsible for the violation of others, ashamed of our bodies and our sexual feelings or function. Shame can be a very painful part of many people's lives.

Shame is a feeling we hold very deep within ourselves. Our mind may have developed an inner voice which has a powerful, critical, judgemental tone.

This voice is a recording of the message we learned from our primary care givers while we were young, and the things it says are negative and damning. It can trigger feelings of unworthiness and shame.

Shame manifests itself in many ways, depending on what our shame is associated with. Were we told off for being vulnerable? For being sexual? Or for simply sharing ourselves – our ideas, thoughts or feelings? Whatever behaviour or facets of our personality and self-expression that we were scolded for as children can trigger shame in us later on.

Shame is a feeling that gets in the way of our self-expression and our self-worth. If we grew up in a place where we weren't supported and loved for who we were, then it's likely that as adults we'll feel ashamed of ourselves in some form.

Shame is hard to talk about. It takes courage to face our shame, but as we explore its triggers and how it affects us, the experience of learned shame can soon subside. With time and healing, we can turn our shame into pride and can learn to value who we are.

"I am very proud to be called a pig. It stands for Pride, Integrity and Guts."
Ronald Reagan

Affirmation: I love and approve of myself, I am proud of all that I am.

Stress

Stress is our body preparing to cope in particular situations. Stressors, the things that we allow to generate stress, can range from life-threatening injuries to exams.

In stressful situations, our fight / flight mechanism kicks in, releasing adrenaline and cortisol into our body. These chemicals increase our alertness and blood pressure – they speed up our heart rate and breathing and give us more energy to cope with our challenge. When we've used up the energy generated, our system should return to normal. (The trouble for us in our culture is that we often sit still and don't use that energy.)

In small doses stress is useful; it keeps us sharp and on our toes, providing us with stamina to get through challenging situations. But prolonged exposure to stress can be harmful.

If the body is unable to return to its normal state, the effects of stress can strain our nervous and immune systems as well as our mind!

Research carried out by the British Psychological Society suggests that people who are exposed to high levels of stress are more likely to experience some form of mental dis-ease (go figure … stress is dis-ease).

We can experience stress as a response to long-term situations as well as individual events. Long-term, low-level stress also weakens the body, depleting our energy resources, so we run on empty and feel tired all the time.

A physical injury or illness can create stress on top of emotional difficulties, relationships and loss.

If you can remain calm, you just don't have all the facts (or you don't care!).

How we manage our commitments and value our time will also determine the level of stress we have in our life. If we're prone to anxiety or depression, we might over-react to stress. Some of us are more sensitive and reactive in stressful situations than others.

We all respond to stress in different ways; some of us may experience panic attacks or feel irritable and tired, some people experience asthma or eczema in response to it, some of us eat or drink to excess. Some of us just lose it (how many times have I wanted to chuck my computer out the window?).

We all have the capacity to manage our stress levels, but sometimes we add to the stress in our lives rather than reducing it.

When we're stressed, it can help us to step back and assess what we might be bringing to the situation. Are we expecting too much of ourselves?

Have we taken too much on? Can we delegate some tasks? Do we need to say No?

Some of the ways we handle stress are to do with our mind, and how we think and approach a situation, rather than the situation itself. Are we managing stress the way our parents taught us? Or can we learn new ways to cope at these times?

It might help to explore how we think in stressful situations. Do we see problems as negative things or new opportunities? Can we break big problems into bite-sized chunks and deal with each piece bit by bit?

"Stress is when you wake up screaming and you realize you haven't fallen asleep yet." Author unknown (he/she sounds stressed out to me, though).

There's lots we can do to , manage our stress; we can learn and improve our self-care and explore our perspectives on things.

To help with stress we can:

- Assess our commitments and time scheduling. Are we taking on too much? What can we change to give ourselves more time to relax and enjoy life?
- Be realistic about what's possible. We don't need to try to be perfect – and we don't have to do everything now.
- Eat a healthy balanced diet; avoid stimulants like coffee, alcohol or nicotine.
- Get enough sleep. During stressful times we can get to bed earlier and wake up earlier – we'll have more time to rest and prepare.
- Get outside in the fresh air, it's good for the brain, and being out in nature often puts things in perspective.
- Learn how to relax – book a massage, take a walk or practise some breathing exercises.
- Take regular exercise. This can help combat stress, but bear in mind that experts state that although exercise is good for stress, over-exercising makes it worse.
- Be kind to ourselves. During stressful periods we need to make sure we make time to do the things we enjoy.
- Take time to ground ourselves, practising deep breathing or meditation; it helps focus and clear the mind.
- Look after our relationships, whether we're stressed or not! During stressful situations we all need support, and we may need space. If our relationships are strong and healthy they can survive the stress and strains of life.

Strokes

The term "stroke" was coined by Eric Berne, founder of Transactional Analysis (he didn't mean the blood clot type!). For him, strokes are units of recognition. For Woollams and Brown (1978) "a stroke is a unit of attention which provides stimulation to an individual". So, the stimulation can be either positive or negative – strokes are either hugs or hurts!

Positive strokes are recognition of who we are or what we've done. Negative strokes are the opposite; they're critical, negative and unsupportive. In the absence of positive strokes, we tend to absorb the negative ones. This can become a pattern to which children are particularly susceptible.

Strokes have a value because they carry emotional energy. Saying "I really like you" carries a high "stroke value", whereas "hello" carries a low one.

There are different kinds of strokes...

Internal strokes are the things we say to ourselves... ...affirmations, self-praise and internal recognition of who we are and what we've done. External strokes come from others, and they're important too.

Conditional strokes are about things, often coming as compliments – "I like your dress." Unconditional strokes are about how people feel about us, when they say, "I like you" or "I love you" (or "I hate you" – best to keep away from strokers like that).

The mind can sometimes filter the strokes we're given, depending on what we believe and feel we deserve. Do we take a compliment – or hear only criticism? Do we acknowledge and absorb praise – or ignore our achievements?

Learning to receive positive strokes – and how to receive them – is important. The more we value and recognise ourselves, the more we'll hear the acknowledgements of others. The more we hear the positive strokes, the less we'll hear the negatives.

"Kindness is more important than
wisdom, and the recognition of this
is the beginning of wisdom."
Theodore Isaac Rubin

Suicide

If we've reached a point where we're thinking about taking our own life, we've lost all hope and feel we can't go on. The sense of hopelessness and despair that evokes suicidal thoughts can seem unfathomable, especially to those who have never had them.

If we've ever had life-taking thoughts, we've been in a dark and deeply lonely place, tough but possible to come back from. Acknowledging we're finding it hard to cope with life is the first step to getting better. If you're feeling suicidal as you read this book, talk to someone. In the UK, Samaritans can be contacted on 08457 909090 (in Ireland it's 1850 609090).

As Samaritans say: "Talking to someone about how we really feel can be like opening a door … it puts you back in control and reveals the choices you have. Whilst it may not be possible to solve all the problems, you can find things to help you look after yourself today."

If we're feeling extremely low and at times suicidal, we may be suffering with depression and might need some help from our doctor. Suicidal feelings can also be the build up of lots of small problems. One on its own may not seem so bad but taken with all the others it may feel too much to bear.

In any case, our doctor may be able to prescribe medication or refer us to a counsellor until we get back on our feet. In the meantime Samaritans are available to help us right now.

In 2007, Samaritans were contacted 2.7 million times; that's an average of five calls a minute.

Samaritans opened the UK's first ever 24-hour phone line in 1953. Since 1984 they've been contacted over 61 million times!

Superego

The term "superego" was developed by Sigmund Freud – the word literally means above the ego.

The concept of the superego belongs to the psychoanalytic school of therapy and refers to the critical part of our mind. This part of our headspace is driven by, or learned from, our parents or primary caregivers.

Learned beliefs, thoughts and behaviour reside in this part of our mind.

S

Therapy

The word "therapy" is Greek in origin; it means cure and heal.

In British society, therapy is a word with many stigmas attached to it. The thought of "going into therapy" terrifies some – but for others of us a therapeutic relationship provides a safe space where we can learn to understand, support and take better care of ourselves.

"We may define therapy as a search for value."
Abraham Maslow

If we're interested in seeing a therapist of any kind, it's important to find someone trained and qualified. It's important we feel safe and comfortable with that person, because we need to feel respected, supported and validated in that relationship.

It's a good idea to meet a couple of therapists before we decide who we want to work with.

The relationship we have with a counsellor or therapist is an important one. We need to feel we can trust that person and can express ourselves openly and honestly.

As this book has outlined, there are all kinds of talking therapies available.

Some of us might need help with our thought process, some with relationships, some of us may need to go back to the past to resolve old patterns and heal old hurts.

We're all different. If we want to see a therapist it's worth taking time to explore what therapy might be best for us and to find the right person for us to work with.

Therapy is not about having someone in our life to tell us what to do; instead therapists are there to support us as we find our own solutions.

Therapy can offer us a space where we can learn new communication skills and ways of relating.

Therapists can help us develop and strengthen our sense of self, explore our values and develop new beliefs.

Therapists can provide us with a place where we can be vulnerable, where we can share our shame, hurts, fears and losses. By confiding in someone who's not part of our life, we can learn to trust and feel understood.

Therapy is not a magic wand. The answers to who we are and why we are lie inside each and every one of us (but sometimes deeply hidden). Sometimes we just need someone who'll hold our world steady as we explore it.

Therapists can provide us with a mirror; they can reflect our world back to us and through this feedback help us develop new insights.

At times we might just need an unconditional listening ear or the support of another person as we make changes in our life. We may need a place to offload, or feel heard and valued by someone impartial.

People see therapists for all kinds of reasons. What we get out of the process comes from what we put into it. Some counselling is available through the NHS (there'll probably be a waiting list) but check with your doctor. If you want to find a therapist there are a number of organisations that can help you find a qualified person at the back of this book.

Therapy is a process of self-discovery, it's not a solution.

Thoughts and thinking

Doctor, Doctor. I think I need glasses...You certainly do, this is a fish and chip shop!

Thoughts are created by electrical impulses in our brain cells; thinking is the process by which we organise our thoughts and make sense of our world.

The process of thinking enables us to organise and respond to our experiences, given our objectives, goals, wants and needs. How we think is about managing and using information.

"All that we are is the result of what we have thought. The mind is everything. What we think we become."
Hindu Prince Siddharta Gautama

Thinking is about recognition. As we meet new experiences we tend to match and file them against our past experiences, and this matching process enables us to judge a situation and respond accordingly.

Our thought patterns and the way we think are largely determined before we are eight years old. The experiences we have during early life become the reference points against which we match and organise our experiences later.

As we grow, we experience new things; this can alter how we think and organise information, but sometimes our thought processes get stuck. We may need to find new ways of thinking and applying our thoughts.

How we think determines how we feel and how we behave, but most of the time we're unaware of how and what we think. Sometimes our thinking is healthy and positive, sometimes it's negative, and sometimes it's a mixture of the two.

"Thought is the sculptor who can create the person you want to be."
Henry David Thoreau

Thoughts are incredibly powerful. Thoughts manifest themselves in our outer world … if we think something bad is going to happen it usually does, but whether it is a bad thing or not is arguable, it depends how we think about it.

Human beings can generate up to 12 000 thoughts a day!

"Make every thought, every fact, that comes into your mind pay you a profit. Make it work and produce for you. Think of things not as they are but as they might be. Don't merely dream but create!" Robert Collier

Transactional Analysis

Transactional Analysis (TA) is a personality and psychotherapeutic theory that was developed by Canadian Eric Berne (1910–1970) during the 1960s.

TA is a form of therapy that encourages personal growth and change. It offers a way of explaining how we are formed psychologically and why we do the things we do.

Part of the TA model describes three ego states: Parent, Adult, and Child. These states also explain how we function and communicate. At any moment we display our personality by experiencing and responding to events through a combination of thoughts, feelings and actions.

In our Parent state, we hold attitudes, feelings and thinking that's in line with the experience of our own parents – be it critical, nurturing, supportive or abusive – and we behave accordingly.

In our Adult state, we respond to a situation in the present moment, the here and now. The Adult part of enables us to access the individual resources that we've learned for ourselves.

In our Child state, we think, behave and feel in the way that we did as a child. Our emotions and instincts are held in this part of our mind.

One of the purposes of TA therapy is to help us explore our different ego states. As we understand them, we can integrate them into our personality in a healthy way whilst developing the strengths of each one.

ADULT

Trauma

"Trauma" is different to "something traumatic". We see traumatic scenes in the news every day, and although these affect us, it's only for a short while. But if we've experienced a trauma ourselves, we meet and deal with it in different ways – its effects can be life-changing, long-lasting and at times debilitating.

A trauma is an experience that causes psychological pain or anxiety, so much so that the event overwhelms our normal coping or defensive strategies.

Abuse of any kind, being involved in a war, having a serious injury, or being attacked or raped are common experiences that result in trauma. Surviving a trauma can lead to severe distress. Survivors of disasters can even experience "survivor guilt" – it's a personal and complex area.

If an experience is traumatic it's sudden, unexpected and outside the ordinary; we feel we can't meet the demands of the experience, and it disrupts or interferes with our frame of reference, our sense of reality.

If we've experienced a traumatic event we may have flashbacks, or painful, disturbing and intrusive memories and/or nightmares, and we may also experience dissociation. We may develop trancelike states, multiple personalities, psychic numbing, or amnesia, as well as depression or anxiety.

What's a trauma for one person may not be for the next; we all meet our experiences and respond to them in different ways. Trauma affects us deeply, and it can change our brain chemistry. If the effects are severe and debilitating, we may be experiencing post-traumatic stress disorder, which can also be treated (see p.282).

Overcoming trauma takes time; we may need medication to cope with its symptoms, and sharing the experience with a trained listener may also help us come to terms with the experience.

Trust

"It takes years to build up trust, and only seconds to destroy it." (Author unknown – can this source be trusted?)

Trust is essential to life, yet sometimes we trust without even thinking. Most of us trust the water we drink is clean, trust the food we eat is safe and trust other drivers as we take to the roads.

"We're never so vulnerable than when we trust someone – but paradoxically, if we cannot trust, neither can we find love or joy." Walter Anderson

Trust is something we learn. If we don't trust, we can't find out if someone is trustworthy. It's one of life's risks. Whether we're trusting or not depends on our experience of the world and our beliefs.

If during childhood our parents or caretakers were untrustworthy, we may find it hard to trust others later.

Our world may feel like a hostile, unpredictable place where we're unable to trust others or trust life itself.

We may feel on guard all the time or as though we always need to be in control. We may think that if we control everything we won't get hurt, upset or caught out (if only life were that simple).

Though it's a risk, it's important to trust others; trust builds intimacy, closeness and understanding. Most of all, however, we need to trust ourselves.

"Trust yourself. You know more than you think you do." Benjamin Spock

If we trust ourselves, we can approach life and relationships with a feeling of confidence. A deep sense of inner trust enables us to take responsibility for our lives, and we can take risks, trusting that whatever happens we will be able to take care of ourselves.

If our sense of trust is damaged as children, or we're misled or betrayed as adults, it can be hard to trust again, but as we develop a sense of inner trust, it will support us as we explore new relationships and experiences.

"Few delights can equal the presence of one whom we trust utterly."
George MacDonald

If we can't trust, we can't experience intimacy, closeness and the support of others. Trust is a risky business but not without its gifts, because as we take new risks we can develop confidence, and as we trust more in others our relationships grow.

We can explore our trust issues with a counsellor or therapist (who we feel we can trust).

Trust is a choice and to some extent a risk but...

"Take into account that great love and great success involve great risk."
Dalai Lama

Truthfulness

"Integrity is telling myself the truth. And honesty is telling the truth to other people."
Spencer Johnson

We learned about truth whilst we were small – from the lessons or lies provided by our elders we found that although telling the truth is about stating how we see things, sometimes we were scolded for doing that.

Our parents often lied about how they were feeling, telling us – often with the best of intentions – that they were okay when really they were angry or sad. But if people choose to protect us from their truth, it can distort our reality and discount our ability to know what we know. You can't argue with the truth … yet so many people try!

What's true for one person might not be so for another. We all see ourselves and the world in different ways. The truth can hurt, and it may take courage to be honest – but the truth is a tool that can help us heal.

The more truthful we are within and without, the more our mind and our sense of identity are strengthened. Our relationship to ourselves within can become much closer, and then, because we have a firm foundation to stand on, we can afford to let our relationships to others become more intimate.

It can be hard to be honest, but it's very empowering. It's a way to be true to ourselves. If we need help asserting ourselves, or need support as we find our own truthful voice, we can talk to a counsellor or therapist.

"We tell lies when we are afraid ... afraid of what we don't know, afraid of what others will think, afraid of what will be found out about us. But every time we tell a lie, the thing that we fear grows stronger."
Tad Williams

TRUTH

"The major task of the twentieth century will be to explore the unconscious, to investigate the subsoil of the mind." Henri Bergson

Unconscious mind

Sigmund Freud was the first to define the unconscious; he believed it was the dustbin of our mind (though for many of us, it's a treasure chest!). For Freud, our unconscious is the place where we hold, bury and suppress painful, unwanted or seemingly unacceptable desires, thoughts and feelings.

Freud believed that most of our behaviour is influenced by our the unconscious processes – the beliefs, hopes and fears we hold that, even though (or especially because) we're not aware of them, influence what we do.

Sometimes, emotionally painful memories or apparently "unacceptable" wishes are diverted into our unconscious.

They get repressed but continue to influence our being, and can reveal themselves in dreams, irrational behaviour, mannerisms or slips of the tongue.

"Your life is the sum result of all the choices you make, both consciously and unconsciously. If you can control the process of choosing, you can take control of all aspects of your life. You can find the freedom that comes from being in charge of yourself."
Robert F. Bennett

For Hargaden and Sills (2002) "feelings are the gateway to our unconscious". As we become aware of our feelings and explore them, they offer us an opportunity to connect, understand and recover our mind.

As we work through old issues and heal our past pain, our mind can become clearer as we clear out old baggage!

Understanding

"There is a great difference between knowing and understanding: you can know a lot about something and not really understand it."
Charles F. Kettering

Understanding is good for the mind, and the mind indeed is what brings it about.

If our mind is experiencing dis-ease, the more we understand what may have caused it, the more we're equipped to recover from it. The more we understand something – whatever it is – the less daunting it is. Information empowers us and can help inform our decisions and choices.

"You don't need strength to let go of something. What you really need is understanding." Guy Finley

If we're experiencing difficulties as we face life's challenges, developing an understanding of what we bring to a situation can be very helpful.

Understanding why we're finding it hard to cope can sometimes release us from our struggle.

Understanding is the gateway to personal freedom. Learning to understand ourselves is the key to unlocking our true potential. Understanding helps us heal our relationships and emotional hurts, and connect to the world in new ways.

The more we understand ourselves, the more self-supporting we become. It's important to both understand and be understanding of who we are and why we are. When we understand why we do the things we do, we can, if we want to, choose to change and do things differently.

As we begin to understand ourselves, we can develop understanding for others; we're all unique and will experience life differently. We can't change people, but we can become more understanding of them.

"Only an open mind can understand, as soon as you think you know your mind is closed."
Understanding

Unipolar affective disorder

Unipolar affective disorder is a term that describes a single emotional state – most commonly depression.

"If we admit our depression openly and freely, those around us get from it an experience of freedom rather than the depression itself."
Dr Rollo May

If we experience this condition, we tend to have severe, debilitating and long-lasting periods of clinical or major depression. Unipolar disorder is sometimes known as clinical or major depression, a mental state we're unable to get out of by ourselves. We can't seem to access any other experience. It affects our work, our relationships, our family and our lives.

If we experience this type of depression we withdraw. We can't enjoy things, our relationships disintegrate, we might go off sex or lose our appetite, and we may experience sleeping problems or want to sleep all the time. We may feel lethargic and isolated, unable to find the energy or ability to cope with a job. At its worst we may attempt suicide.

Unipolar disorder is a serious illness. Although the causes are unclear and could be varied, it's a treatable condition. The first point of call is our doctor.

Medication can be important to treating the illness, and talking to a counsellor or mental health worker can provide us with support as we begin to get better.

“Depression is nourished by a lifetime of ungrieved and unforgiven hurts.”
Penelope Sweet

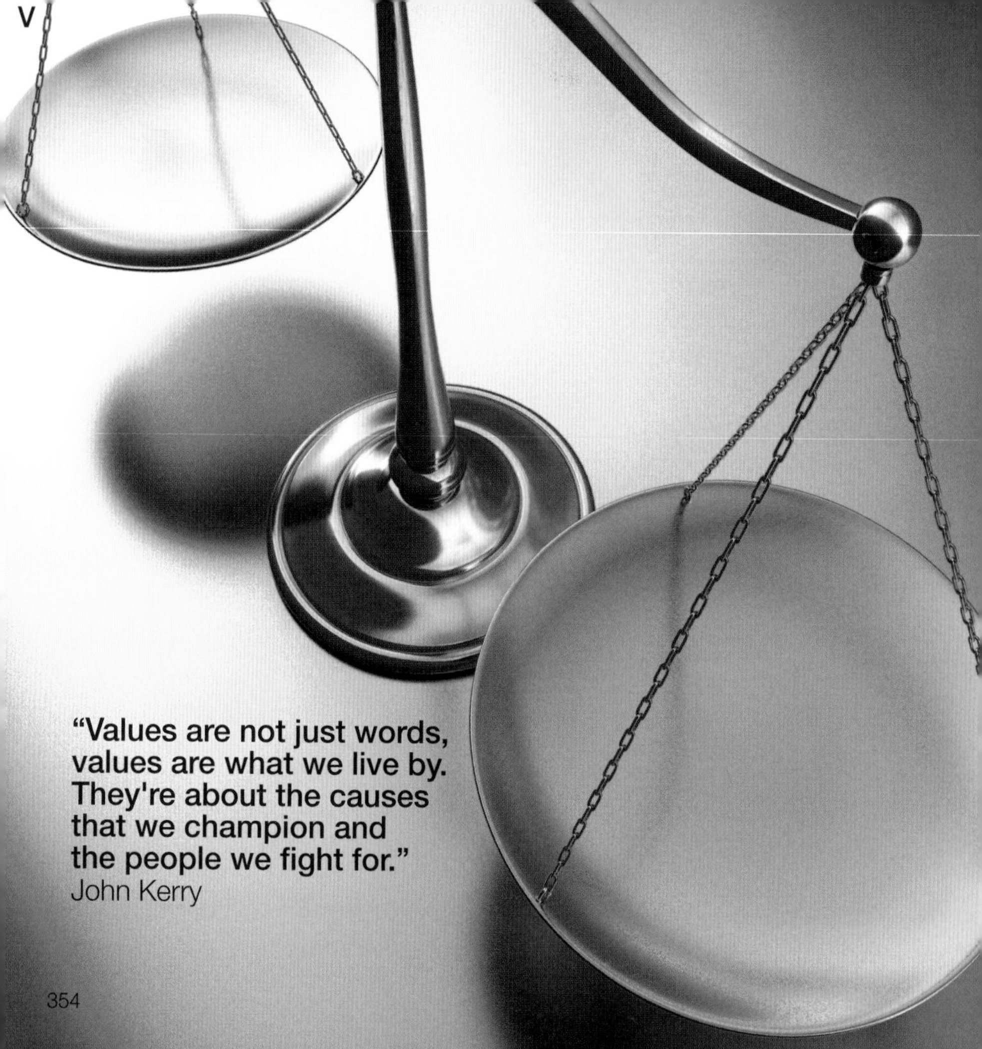

"Values are not just words, values are what we live by. They're about the causes that we champion and the people we fight for."
John Kerry

Values

Values are important to us. Whether we're aware of them or not, the values we hold and the qualities they inspire can strengthen our individuality and our state of mind. Valuing who we are is the first and most important value.

Our values are the principles, ideas and beliefs we hold about the things that matter to us. Our values – when we're aware of them – can change, especially as we grow. Our values tend to inform the way we go about doing things, and they inform our individual sense of what's right or wrong.

Just like our beliefs, our values were formed in childhood. What we were taught to value then might be very different to what we value now. Some of the values we learned may not match who we are any more, and as we explore what matters as adults we can shake off our old values and give ourselves new ones.

As we become clear about our values, they can give us a framework which can inform our decisions, actions and choices. As we honour our values, we honour ourselves; our values can guide us and give our life more meaning.

Being clear about what matters to us can enhance our state of mind. Although we can't always control what happens to us in life, our value system can guide us as we respond to life's events. If we value kindness and fairness, we can respond to situations in a kind and fair way.

Values help us separate what matters to us and what doesn't matter, what's important to us and what's not. Once we've made up our mind about the big things in life, we can let the little things fall away.

Wants and needs

We all want different things from life. Most of what we want we can have … all we need to do is just make up our mind and go for it!

Wants are desires, they inform our decision making. What we want can become a goal and something to work towards.

Knowing what we want from life is helpful to our state of mind. If we take time to ask ourselves what we want, the answers can focus our energy, refine the choices we make and alter our life path. If we believe we can have what we want then we've kind of got it already!

"Any so-called material thing that you want is merely a symbol: you want it not for itself, but because it will content your spirit for the moment." Mark Twain

Sometimes we attach feelings to wants, thinking that by getting what we want we'll feel happier – we say things like "I'd be happy if I could..." or "If only I had..."

"If you want to live a happy life, accept what is and aspire to what will be."
Darren Bottrill

Feeling good about life and ourselves is something we can't buy. It's something we find within. Happiness and contentment are states of being rather than having. When we're happy we can live in the moment, and when we live in the moment we're happy.

Desires and wants are based in the future – they're things to aim for in the short term – but longer-term happiness exists in our hearts.

"You can't always get what you want – but if you try sometimes, you might find you get what you need."
The Rolling Stones

Needs are more fundamental to life than wants are. Knowing what we need is good for our mind. All of us need food, warmth, shelter and, in this society, money - these are the basics. Once we've met these basic needs we can consider whether there's anything else we need from life or from others in order to feel fulfilled and happy.

In order to take care of ourselves, it's important to be aware of our individual needs. What one person needs to feel okay will be different from what another needs.

Having needs is not "neediness". We all have needs – they can be as fundamental as needing to eat and sleep every day and as important as needing human contact and recognising and releasing our potential as a person.

Most of us have the capacity to meet our needs ourselves, from within. But if we rely on others to do things for us or to make us feel good, then we're constantly at the mercy of others and probably in a codependent relationship. This is neediness.

Once we know we can meet our needs within, we can become more independent, self-fulfilled and autonomous. We can ask others to help us without being dependent on them.

Others can then choose to help us, and approaching ourselves and others in this way is much more liberating: it fosters co-operation, teamwork and partnership – where we all work together to get our needs met.

Withdrawal

The word "withdrawal" has a number of meanings in terms of wellbeing.

If we've become addicted or dependent on a chemical substance such as nicotine, cannabis, heroin or prescribed medication, we may need to go through a withdrawal period.

Chemical withdrawal allows our body to detoxify, ridding itself of the chemical substances we've become addicted to. It can be a challenging but very necessary part of healing and recovery from dependency … it's the first part of the withdrawal process.

But as well as withdrawing chemically, we sometimes need to withdraw emotionally or physically. This can be both healthy and unhealthy. At times we need to remove ourselves from situations in order to recharge our batteries, protect our feelings and take care of ourselves.

If people or events are causing us distress, we can choose to withdraw, stepping back and taking time to review things, find solutions, heal or consider what's best to do next. This type of withdrawal is important and healthy.

"You cannot be lonely if you like the person you're alone with." Wayne Dyer

At other times, especially if we're experiencing depression or emotional or psychological difficulties, we might withdraw from life.

We might not want to be part of social situations – but the trouble is, with too much time alone to dwell on the past, we can end up feeling isolated, alone and unhappy.

This kind of withdrawal is not so helpful!

"Through loyalty to the past, our mind refuses to realise that tomorrow's joy is possible only if today's makes way for it … each wave owes the beauty of its line only to the withdrawal of the preceding one."
André Gide

Psychological withdrawal is often associated with trauma. If we're feeling a little withdrawn or have prolonged episodes when we can't engage in everyday life, it might be an idea to talk to our doctor, as we might be depressed or experiencing anxiety. We may need some chemical or emotional support to get us back on our feet.

Choosing when to withdraw and when to engage in life is all part of maintaining a healthy state of mind; we probably know what's best for us even if it's sometimes difficult for us to recognise it.

At times we need to be with ourselves to heal, reflect or do our own thing, whereas at other times we need the company, intimacy and enjoyment of others.

Workaholic

"A workaholic – someone who can't afford a pint."

Though "workaholic" is not a medical term, we all know of people who find it hard to maintain a healthy work–life balance. As a workacholic, we seek and get our recognition for what we "do" rather than "who" we are.

At times in our life, our career can be the focus of all that we do, and we sometimes define ourselves through our work. Our job can give our life meaning, structure, routine and a sense of achievement.

Sometimes, however, we can bury ourselves in our work as a way of avoiding what's going on at home, or anywhere outside our workplace. We use our work as a distraction rather than face family or relationship problems.

When our work is our life, we might be lacking a little balance. We might overwork because we feel lonely.

We may have moved to a new place for a job but haven't made new friends yet, and we may only feel confident about ourselves through our work … this is what makes us workaholics!

How we work, how much we work and our attitude to work is important for our mind. Work can be creative, rewarding and fun, but it can also exhaust us and be a trigger for our stress.

Some of us may have the tendency to want to please others through our work. We may find it hard to say No. Our work may be the means by which we gain our sense of self-worth. We may feel we have to work hard to feel good about ourselves, and to feel accepted and approved of.

Our work and careers are important to us but it's better to see them as just a part of our life. We may need to work through our work issues at times. We're all valuable just as we are, not just because of what we do.

Affirmation: I am valuable and important just as I am, I approve of myself.

Young people and mental health

Young people are affected by life just as much as adults, sometimes more so. Our younger people are more vulnerable, as their minds are still growing.

As they navigate puberty and the challenges of adolescence, they are still developing their values, security and sense of belonging in themselves and the world.

Young people are just as prone to mental illness as adults, but they may find it harder to ask for help or even be unaware that help is available. The adult world can seem a daunting place to them – our elders and teachers can give us strong messages about life which are not always realistic, positive or true.

Parents, teachers, caregivers and the media, whether they mean to or not, perpetuate messages that affect the minds of our young people. Younger people are still developing their sense of reality.

Their limited experience may not have provided them with the objectivity, detachment or filtering processes we use as adults.

Make no mistake, the way our young people see themselves and the world will be influenced by us, the adults and authority figures that surround and support them.

- If we want our young people to be positive, then let's be positive with them.
- If we want our young people to feel confident, let's tell them they can do it.
- If we want our kids to love themselves, then tell them they're loved and likable.
- If we want our youngsters to feel good about themselves, let's tell them how good they are just as they are.
- If we want our children to like and enjoy life, allow them to like and enjoy themselves – and let's like and enjoy them, too.

Though not in every case – depending on a child's background or educational experience – most of our young people are growing up in an environment where the predominant message is one of fear or lacking. The news is full of it …

… there're not enough jobs, not enough resources, not enough homes, not enough money, there's a paedophile on every corner, recreation fields are for yobs, if you wear a hoodie you're probably violent, the world is unsafe, life is hard, so if you want to get on get your head down: you're lucky if you can enjoy it …

It's no wonder more young people are being admitted to hospital now because of alcohol abuse than ever before.

According to government figures published in February 1999 by the Mental Health Foundation, approximately 20% of all adolescents have some form of mental health problem, including eating disorders. And at the time of writing, that's nearly a decade ago. Things appear to be a lot worse now, near the end of the noughties.

If you're a young person, or know of a young person or are bringing one up, there's plenty of information and advice available about the kinds of mental illnesses that affect young people and how to get help if it's needed.

A word about words

I hope this book has been helpful to you – encouraging, informative, meaningful and positive. I hope the words I've used have been accessible, easy to understand, sensitive and supportive.

If you're overcoming a mental illness, are recovering from addiction, or have experienced loss or need a change of direction, I hope the words in here give you hope, inspire you and encourage you in your journey.

Words are very powerful, especially the words we say to ourselves. The words we use have the power to heal or hurt us – and our words affect others in just the same way. Words create our worlds; words are manifestations (and make no mistake).

The words we choose to use are the bridge between our inner world and our outer world.

Much of what we know, feel and have learned right now is because of words – the words we heard from others (or didn't) that informed us as children, and the words we use today as we grow in ourselves (and grow our children). Well, these are my last words (for this book anyway!).

Words can build people just as quick as they break them.

Words can build bridges, but only if we let them.

Words can create as quick as they destroy.

Words can make us laugh, they can also annoy.

But every word's a gift, a precious lovely thing,

So careful how you use them, you don't know what they'll bring!

pleasant: *His vicio*
lovable of men. \ *a*
love[1] /lʌv/ *n* **1** [U
another person,
close friends: *a*
hate, hatred 2
ual attraction:
other). \ *They fe*

A word about the "talking cure"

Over the years it has been a great privilege for me to support people through their struggle to overcome emotional distress. It takes courage to acknowledge emotional dis-ease, as mental health still lives in a place of misunderstanding and fear.

It also takes courage to walk through hospital doors to undergo surgery, but we manage with support and encouragement.

We may get to see images of the "problem", or even see the offending part itself. We have something tangible to look at and this helps our understanding, acceptance and resolve to heal.

But the mind, that wonderful part of the most complicated organ in our body, the place of our intellect, reason, understanding and spirit, our essential being, is rarely given the care it both needs and deserves.

This "being" is very very resilient. It is capable of truly amazing endurance and adaptation and it is also capable of growth and change.

One of the most important parts of being human is that we are all capable of emotional growth and the key to this seems to be a willingness to consider change.

Change can feel uncomfortable and challenging, but at the core of this process lies hope, which is the fuel of conviction that we can change.

If you are reading this book you have a mind. If you are suffering any of the discomfort or distress it describes, then get the understanding and support you need in order to achieve and protect your good mental health and well being.

Talking therapy can help you to discover the likely cause of your feelings, and there is almost always a cause.

Through awareness and understanding we become able to reconsider and re-evaluate, and as Emma has found, the more we understand about our mind and ourselves, the more power we have for change.

There is no magic or intrigue in what we do as therapists, just a great deal of preparation, training, supervision and strict rules which help us to keep you safe.

Just as you would only trust your physical body to a competent person, please ensure that the person you trust with your mind is qualified, competent, and registered with an ethical regulatory body.

Above all I hope that Emma's words will encourage and inspire you to take your own journey to emotional freedom and health.

Marilyn Jope,
Counsellor.

Bodmin 01208 831473
www.counsellingcornwall.co.uk

Acknowledgements & recognition

This book is dedicated to and in recognition of everyone who works in the field of mental health.

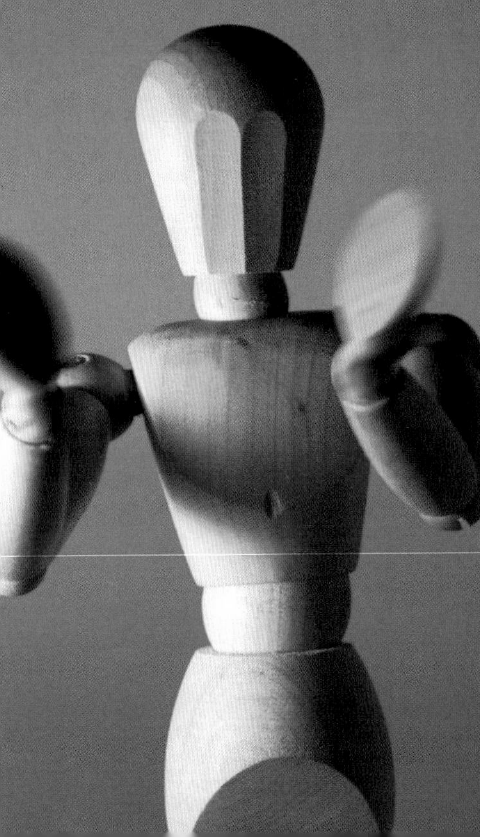

I'd like to thank the authors, therapists, doctors, mental health workers and the many organisations that have contributed to this book. Their words, theories, experience and understanding of the human mind has been inspirational. Above all I admire their faith, faith in the human spirit and faith that with time, appropriate support and treatment, most of us can overcome our mental dis-ease, reclaim our true selves and get our heads round our mind.

Thank you to Marilyn Jope, counsellor, for her support, enthusiasm and commitment to this book, a warm and whole-hearted woman who's dedicated to her work in the field of mental health. Bodmin 01208 831473. www.counsellingcornwall.co.uk

Thank you to Janine Fahri, for her wise words about food and mood and her continued belief in this book. www.nutrilifeclinic.com NutrilLife Clinic 07956 848002

Thank you to inspirational therapist and trainer Jaki Beddingham and her training team. www.aaaib.co.uk

Thank you to Dr Anna Gevers, St Lawrences Mental Health Unit, Bodmin, for her belief in this book and help with the psychiatric and medical terms.

Finally, thanks to Darren Bottrill, for reminding me this book was a "brilliant idea". I am grateful for his support and commitment to me and this book and for being on the end of an email throughout it's evolution. Future Days Counselling and Psychotherapy 01726 77569 or Nightlink 0808 8000 306.

I'd like to thank my parents, my brother and all of my friends for their continued encouragement and support while I've written this book. They understand I need space to get my head down and write and are always there when I put my pen (well PC) down.

I'd like to thank Claire England at Leap – Design for Change for her outstanding design efforts and interpretation.

Also, Shelley Fletcher for her PR and communications genius at Deborah Clarke Associates, Caroline Petherick for her magic words and Sue Lightfoot for her proofing and patience with the index! Also thanks to David Meneer, Deborah Clarke, Jon Hart, Matt Hocking and Scott Coning.

Above all, I'd like to thank all the organisations especially BACP, ADDISS, MIND, Rethink, Samaritans, AFT, Relate, B-eat, MDF and Action on Addiction for allowing me to use their information, research and statistics in this publication.

Where possible we've tried to credit, attribute and reference all the sources used to create this book. Every effort has been made to ensure the information in here is correct and up to date. But… like life! We don't ways get it right first time. Don't hesitate to contact me with any changes or amends for future editions of this book.

DIRECTORY OF ORGANISATIONS.

Addiction

Alcoholics Anonymous
www.alcoholics-anonymous.org.uk
0845 769 7555

Action on Addiction
www.actiononaddiction.org.uk
0845 126 4130

AddAction
www.addaction.co.uk
0207 251 5860

Al-Anon
www.al-anon.org.uk
0207 403 0888

Gamblers anonymous
www.gamblersanonymous.org.uk
0207 384 3040

Give up smoking NHS
www.nhs.uk/gosmokefree
0800 022 4332

Narcotics anonymous
www.ukna.org
020 7730 0009

ADHD

Addiss
www.addiss.co.uk 020 8592 2800

Anger

British Association of Anger Management
www.angermanage.co.uk
0845 130 286

Anorexia nervosa

Beat Eating Disorders
www.b-eat.co.uk
0845 6341414

National Centre for Eating Disorders
www.eating-disorders.org.uk
0845 838 2040

Anxiety

First Steps to Freedom
www.first-steps.org 0845 120 2916

National Phobics Society
www.phobics-society.org.uk
0870 770 456

No Panic
www.nopanic.org 0808 8080545

Art therapy

British Art Therapists
www.baat.org 020 7686 4216

Assertiveness

Learn Direct
www.learndirect.co.uk
08000 150 450

Bereavement

Cruse Bereavement Care
www.crusebereavementcare.org.uk
0844 4779400

Child Bereavement Charity
www.childbereavement.org.uk
01494 446648

Bipolar affective disorder

The Bi-Polar Organisation
www.mdf.org.uk
08456 340 540

Body dysmorphic disorder

Dr David Veale
www.veale.co.uk

OCD Action
www.ocdaction.org.uk
0207 226 4000

Bodywork therapy

Society of Teachers of Alexander Technique
www.stat.org.uk 0845 230 7828

Association of Reflexologists
www.aor.org.uk 01823 351010

The Institute for Complementary Medicine
www.i-c-m.org.uk 0207 922 7980

The British Acupuncture Council
www.acupuncture.org.uk
020 8735 0400

Federation of Holistic Therapies
www.fht.org.uk
0844 875 2022

British Wheel of Yoga
www.bwy.org.uk 01529 306851

Iyengar Yoga Association
www.iyengar.org.uk
0208 269 2595

Bulimia nervosa

B-eat Eating Disorders
www.b-eat.co.uk 0845 6341414

Disordered Eating
www.disordered-eating.co.uk

Nat Cen. Eating Disorders
www.eating-disorders.org.uk
0845 838 2040

Clinical psychologists

British Psychological Society
www.bps.org.uk 0116 254 9568

Counsellors and psychotherapists

British Association of Counselling & Psychotherapy
www.bacp.co.uk 01455 883300

British Association of Behavioural & Cognitive Therapists
www.babcp.com 0161 797 4484

UK Register of Counsellors and Psychotherapists
www.ukrconline.org.uk 01455 883300

British Association Of Play Therapists
www.bapt.info 01932 828638

UK Council for Psychotherapy
www.psychotherapy.org.uk
020 7014 9955

Association of Family Therapists
www.aft.org.uk 01925 44414

Institute of Family Therapy
www.instituteoffamilytherapy.org.uk
020 7391 9150

Dementia

Alzheimers Society
www.alzheimers.org.uk
0845 300 0336

Dementia Care Partnership
www.dementiacare.org.uk
0191 217 1323

Depression

Depression Alliance
www.depressionalliance.org.
0845 123 23 20

The Samaritans
www.samaritans.org
08457 909090

Dissociative disorders

Dissociation World
www.dissociation-world.org.uk
0870 005 3273

BDP World
www.bdpworld.org.uk
0870 005 3273

Emotional abuse

Hidden Hurt
www.hiddenhurt.co.uk

Refuge www.refuge.org.uk
0808 2000 247

Muslim Women's Helpline
www.mwhl.org 0208 904 8193

Jewish Women's Aid
www.jwa.org.uk 0800 591203

Somalian's Women's Centre
020 8752 1787

Chinese information and Advice Centre
www.caic.co.uk 020 7692 3697

Black Association of Women: Step Out
029 2043 7390

National Centre of Domestic Violence
www.ncdc.org.uk 08709 220704

Women's Aid Federation of England
www.womensaid.org.uk 0117 944 4411

Network for Surviving Stalking
www.nss.org.uk 0845 30 30 900

Men's Advice Line
www.mensadviceline.org.uk
0808 801 0327

Male Perpetutor Programmes
www.respect.uk.net 0845 122 8609

Gay/bi-sexual/transsexual abuse
www.brokenrainbow.org.uk
08452 604460

Existential therapy

Society of Existential Analysis
www.existentialanalysis.co.uk

Family therapy

Association of Family Therapists
www.aft.org.uk 01925 444414

Institute of Family Therapy
020 7391 9150

Food and mood

British Association of Applied Nutrition & Nutritional Therapists
www.bant.org.uk
08706 061284

General mental health organisations

Mind
www.mind.org.uk
0845 766 0163

Rethink
www.rethink.org
0845 456 0455

SANE
www.sane.org.uk
0845 767 8000

Mental Health Foundation
www.mentalhealth.org

Samaritans
www.samaritans.org
08457 909090

Gestalt

Gestalt Psychotherapy and Training Institute. www.pgti.org.uk

Grief

Cruse Bereavement Care
www.crusebereavementcare.org.uk
0844 4779400

Child Bereavement Charity
www.childbereavement.org.uk
01494 446648

Group analysis

Institute of Group Analysts
www.groupanalysis.org.uk
0207 431 2693

Hypnotherapy

National Council for Hypnotherapy
www.hypnotherapists.org.uk
0800 756 6375

UK Confederation of Hypnotherapy Organisations
www.ukcho.co.uk 0800 952 0560

Insomnia

Insomniac UK
www.insomniacs.co.uk

Memory loss

Alzheimers Society
www.alzheimers.org.uk

Music therapy

British Society of Music Therapy
www.bsmt.org

Association of Professional Music Therapists
www.apmt.org
0208 4404153

NLP

Association for NLP
www.anlp.org
0845 053 1162

OCD

OCD Action
www.ocdaction.org.uk
0207 226 4000

OCD UK
www.ocduk.org
Admin 0845 120 3778

Overeating disorder

Beat Eating Disorders
www.b-eat.org.uk
0845 634 1414

National Centre for Eating Disorders
www.eatingdisorders.org.uk
0845 838 2040

Panic attacks

No Panic
www.nopanic.org
0808 808 0545

First Steps to Freedom
www.first-steps.org
0845 120 2916

Paranoia

Hearing Voices Network
www.hearing-voices.org
0845 122 8641

Personality disorders

National Personality Disorder Website
www.personalitydisorder.org.uk

Phobias

National Phobic Society
www.phobics-society.org.uk
0870 122 2325

National Organisation for Phobias, Anxiety, Neurosis, info and Care
www.nopanic.org.uk
0808 808 0545

Triumph Over Phobia
www.triumphoverphobia.com
0845 6009601

Dental Anxiety and Phobia Association
www.healthyteeth.com
0207 935 0892

Physical abuse

National Domestic Abuse Helpline
0808 2000 247

Refuge
www.refuge.org 0808 2000 247

Rape Crisis www.rapecrisis.org.uk

Victim Support
www.victimsupport.org.uk
0845 3030 900

Post-traumatic stress disorder

ASSIST
01788 560 800

First Person Plural
www.firstpersonplural.org.uk

Ex-Services Mental Welfare
www.combatstress.com
01372 841600

Medical Foundation for Victims of Torture
www.torturecare.org.uk
020 7813 7777

Refugee Support Centre
020 7820 3606

Vicitim Support Helpline
0845 303 0900

PTSD for ex-servicemen and women
www.ptsd.org.uk

UK Trauma Group
www.uktrauma.org.uk

Postnatal depression

The Association for Post Natal Illness
www.apni.org
0207 386 0868

National Childbirth Trust
www.nctpregnancyandbabycare.com
0870 444 8709

Perinatal Illness UK
www.pni-uk.com

Meet a Mum Association
www.mama.co.uk

Family Welfare Association
www.fwa.org.uk
0207 254 6251

Home Start
www.home-start.org.uk
0800 068 6368

Fatherhood Institute
www.fatherhoodinstitute.org

Depression during Pregnancy
www.depression-in-pregnancy.org.uk

Birth Trauma Association
www.birthtraumaassociation.org.uk

Psychiatry

Royal College of Psychiatrists
www.rcpsych.ac.uk
020 7235 2351

Psychoanalysis

Royal College of Psychoanalysis
www.psychoanalysis-cpuk.org
01799 584231

British Psychoanalytical Society
www.psychoanalysis.org.uk
020 7563 5000

Relationship counselling

Relate
www.relate.org.uk 0300 100 1234

Marriage Care
www.marriagecare.org.uk
0845 660 6000

Couples Counselling Network
www.ukcouplescounselling.com

Seasonal affective disorder

Lumie
www.lumie.com 01954 780500

The Seasonal Affective Disorder Association
www.sada.org.uk

Schizophrenia

Hearing Voices Network
www.hearing-voices.org
0845 122 8641

Self-harm

Childline
www.childline.org.uk 0800 1111

Childline self-harm pages
www.selfharm.org.uk

National Self-harm Network
www.nshn.co.uk

Self-harm Alliance
www.selfharmalliance.org
01242 578820

The Samaritans
www.samaritans.org
08457 909090

Sexual abuse

Rape and Sexual Abuse Support Centre
www.rasasc.bizview.co.uk
08451 221 331

Women's Aid
www.womensaid.org.uk 0808 2000 247

Inconfidence
www.inconfidence.org

Rape Crisis England and Wales
www.rapecrisis.org.uk

Respond
www.respond.org.uk 0808 808 0700

Support4U
www.support4u.org.uk

Sexuality

Relate
www.relate.org.uk
0300 100 1234

Suicide

The Samaritans
www.samaritans.org
08457 909090

PAPYRUS
www.papyrus-uk.org
08000 684141

Survivors of bereavement by suicide
www.uk-sobs.org.uk
0844 561 6855

Support for Carers

Carers UK
www.carersuk.org
0808 808 7777

Transactional analysis

Institute of Transactional Analysis
www.ita.org.uk

Unipolar affective disorder

Clinical Depression
www.clinical-depression.co.uk

Young people and mental health

Young Minds
www.youngminds.org.uk
0800 018 2138 for parents

Childline
www.childline.org.uk
0800 1111

Bibliography, references and further reading

Berne, Dr Eric. *Games People Play,* Penguin Books, USA, 1964.

Berne, Dr Eric. *Sex In Human Loving,* Penguin Books, USA, 1970.

Berry, Ruth. *Jung - A Beginners Guide,* Hodder & Stoughton, 2005.

Bowlby John. *Attachment and Loss* Volume 1, Pimlico, London, 1997.

Bowlby, John. *The Making and Breaking of Affectional Bonds*, Routledge, London, 2007.

Bradshaw, John. *Healing the Shame That Binds Us,* Health Communications, Florida, 2006.

Carper, Jean. *Food: your miracle medicine,* Simon & Schuster Ltd, 1995.

Coleman, Andrew. *A Dictionary of Psychology,* Oxford University Press, Oxford, 2006.

Dayton, Tian, PhD. *Heartwounds*, Health Communications, Inc. Florida, 1997.

De Mello, Anthony. *Awareness,* Zondervan, Michigan, 2002.

De Mello, Anthony. *The Way To Love,* Doubleday, New York, 1995.

Diamond, Milton. *Sex Watching.* Guild Publishing, London, 1986.

Gawain, Shakti. *Living in the Light*. New World Library, California, 1986.

Gilbert, Paul. *Overcoming Depression,* Oxford University Press, Oxford, 2000.

Gross, Richard D. *Psychology.* 2nd Edition, Hodder and Stoughton, London, 1999.

Hamilton, David R' PhD. *It's the Thought That Counts,* Hay House, 2006.

Harris, Dr Thomas A. *I'm Okay, You're Okay,* Arrow Books, London, 1995.

Hay, Louise L. *The Power Is Within You,* Eden Grove Editions, 1991.

Houston, Gaie. *The Now Red Book of Gestalt,* 1995 Edition, Gaie Houston, London.

Illsley Clarke, Jean & Dawson, Connie. *Growing Up Again,* Hazelden, Minnesota, 1998.

Kirschenbaum, Howard & Land Henderson, Valerie. *The Carl Rogers Reader,* Houghton Mifflin, Company, New York, 1989.

McDermott, Ian & O'Connor, Joseph. *The Way of NLP.* Thorsons, 2001.

Steiner, Claude. *Emotional Literacy,* Personhood Press, 2003.

Steiner, Claude. *Scripts People Live,* 2nd Edition, Grove Press, New York, 1990.

Stewart, Ian & Joines, Vann. *TA Today,* Lifespace Publishing, 1987.

Storr, Anthony. *Freud*, Oxford University Press, Oxford, 1989.

Sutton, Jan & Stewart, William. *Learning to Counsel,* 2nd Edition, How To Books, Oxford, 2002.

Tilney, Tony. *Dictionary of Transactional Analysis,* Wiley Blackwell, 1998.

Whitfield, Dr Charles L. *Healing the Child Within,* Health Communications, Florida, 1987.

Index

Future Days
Counselling and Psychotherapy
St Austell, Cornwall
01726 75569

Deborah Clark and Associates
01208 77900

Cornwall Counselling
www.cornwallcounselling.co.uk
Bodmin, Cornwall

Magic Words
www.magic-words.co.uk

Nightlink
Cornwall's Emotional Support Helpline
Freephone 0808 8000 306

Nutrilife Clinic
Nutrition & Lifestyle
07956 848 002
www.nutrilifeclinic.com